The ULTIMATE
TRIVIA
Quizbook

The
ULTIMATE

TRIVIA
Quizbook

Compiled by

Fid Backhouse & Richard Widdows

Illustrations by Mike Webb

BROCKHAMPTON
PRESS

CONTENTS

Continued overleaf ➤ ➤ ➤ ➤ ➤ ➤ ➤ ➤ ➤ ➤

CONTENTS

ANSWERS START ON PAGE 204

Beat Knowall at his own game (with a little help from Bonzo)

I'M PRETTY HOT !!!

BUT NOT AS HOT AS ME.

Knowall thinks he's brilliant, but unfortunately he always gets his answers wrong. Enjoy beating him at his own game by answering Knowall's questions correctly . . . with a little help from Bonzo, who'll always give you a clue to the right answer.

QUIZ NUMBER 1

Knowall's question:

Where may the Islets of Langerhans be found?

EUROPE !!!

1 Through the streets of which city is Lady Godiva said to have ridden naked?

2 Which new international language was created by Ludovic Lazarus Zamenhof in the 1880s?

3 What word is used to describe a grotesque carving of an animal, man or devil?

4 When was Samuel Morse's dot-dash alphabet first introduced: 1821, 1829, 1838, 1845, 1857?

5 Which 11th-century sect of Shi'ite Muslim fanatics pledged themselves to murder non-believers?

6 Although he led a plot to kill James 1, Robert Catesby is not as well remembered as which co-plotter?

7 Which declaration binds doctors to observe a strong code of medical ethics?

8 What is the name given to carbon dioxide when it is frozen to $-78.5°C$ ($-173.3°F$)?

9 During the Boer War, who commanded the garrison of Mafeking, relieved in May 1900 after a long siege?

10 In Jerusalem, what sacred monument stands on the site of King Solomon's Temple, destroyed in 70AD?

11 Name the gruelling test of stamina which takes place at Aintree in late March or early April each year.

12 Which three famous fictional characters lived at 221B Baker Street, London?

13 What was the epic raft voyage across the Pacific by Norwegian explorer Thor Heyerdahl called?

14 Who was crowned as Holy Roman Emperor on Christmas Day in 800AD?

15 In what war did *Monitor* and *Merrimack* become the first "ironclad" battleships to fight each other?

16 When were the last convicts deported from Britain to Australia: 1837, 1852, 1861, 1873, 1885?

17 In 1865, who left his work as a Methodist minister to form the Salvation Army?

18 At what US Army facility near Louisville, Kentucky are the USA's gold reserves held?

19 In 1720, what speculative venture brought ruin to thousands of wealthy families in England?

20 In 1957, a German engineer demonstrated the rotary piston engine which bears his name. Who was he?

21 What is the name of the wave which sweeps up the Severn estuary and river?

22 What great hero of Saxon resistance to the Normans in the 11th century was based on the Isle of Ely?

23 What handy item was invented by Swede Johan Edvard Lundström in 1855?

24 Exactly where in London can the famous Whispering Gallery be found?

25 Which creek in North-West Canada was the scene of a great gold rush at the end of the 19th century?

26 What is the artistic significance of the painting *The Battle of Gettysburg* by Paul Philippotaeus?

27 What is the literary significance of Juan Fernández island off the coast of Chile?

28 What do the five interlinked rings on the flag of the Olympic Movement represent?

29 In 1775, who made a famous ride to warn colonists of Massachusetts that British troops were on the way?

30 In 1996, which tennis "great" made his professional golf debut on the European tour in the Czech Open?

Answers on page 204

QUIZ NUMBER 2

Knowall's question:

According to legend, how many knights sat at the Round Table at the court of King Arthur?

FIFTY !!!

1 How many cubic centimetres in a cubic metre?

2 Who reached No. 4 with *You're Sixteen* in 1974?

3 How many steps are there in John Buchan's novel?

4 Which country is divided into 23 "cantons"?

5 What is Chanel's most celebrated perfume?

6 How many dalmatians featured in Dodie Smith's book?

7 What measures 1,760 yards?

8 Which wedding anniversary is signified by china?

9 What comes next: 2, 3, 5, 7, 11, 13, 17, 19?

10 Which element has the atomic number 1?

11 What is 40% of 40?

12 How many cards are in a tarot pack: 60, 66, 72, 78?

13 Of what are 6, 28 and 496 the smallest examples?

14 What are the two numbers used in the binary system?

15 How old is an institution celebrating a quincentenary?

16 If you throw a six with a dice, what is the total of the four other visible faces?

17 Which of Walt Disney's seven dwarfs is missing: Doc, Grumpy, Sneezy, Sleepy, Happy, Dopey?

18 Which Republic has existed in France since 1958: Second, Third, Fourth, Fifth, Sixth?

19 The western *The Magnificent Seven* (1970) was based on which traditional Japanese tale?

20 How many green bottles are there on the wall before the first one "should accidentally fall"?

21 What number do you ring to find out who has called you when you were not available?

22 What is one-tenth of a nautical mile: a fathom, a cable, a knot, a league?

23 According to The Book of Revelations, what is "the number of the Beast"?

24 Why was 29 bad news for Anne Boleyn (1536), Percy Bysshe Shelley (1822) and Mrs Beeton (1865)?

25 What notorious event took place at 875 South Bundy Drive, Los Angeles in June 1994?

26 How many decibels is the noise of heavy traffic: 65-70, 70-75, 75-80, 80-85, 85-90?

27 What was banned by the 18th Amendment to the US Constitution, passed 1920 and repealed 1933?

28 How many "leagues under the sea" did Captain Nemo travel in Jules Verne's 1870 story?

29 What do 9,192,631,770 cycles of caesium vibratum represent *(in time you'll work it out!)*?

30 The drinkers of which Australian lager wouldn't "give a XXXX for anything else"?

ONE'S COMPANY, THREE'S A CROWD.

Answers on page 204

Knowall's question:

What is the atomic number of silver?

IT MUST BE 74 !!!

1 How many hours from Tulsa was Gene Pitney in 1963?

2 What is 9.30pm on the "24-hour clock"?

3 In which countries is Anzac Day marked on 29 April?

4 What is the last of the year's four Quarter Days?

5 On which day does the grouse shooting season open?

6 What do the initials GMT and BST stand for?

7 Which famous person was killed on 22 November 1963?

8 What day in England is St George's Day?

9 Which month is named after the Roman god of war?

10 How did Boxing Day get its name?

11 At 12 noon GMT, what is the time in New York?

12 What do the letters "am" and "pm" stand for?

13 Which material marks a 13th wedding anniversary?

14 In France, what date is celebrated as Bastille Day?

15 Which day precedes Ash Wednesday?

16 What crucial world championships are held on Good Friday at Tinsley Green in Sussex?

17 Julius Caesar was murdered by Cassius and Brutus on the "Ides of March". Which day is it?

18 How long does it take for the Earth to travel 1½ million miles: a day, a week, a month, a year?

19 Which festival is celebrated by both Anglican and Roman Catholic churches on 1 November?

20 What are the two times of year when the Sun is overhead at the Tropics of Cancer and Capricorn?

21 What date in Britain is Poppy Day, commemorating those service personnel who were killed in war?

22 What takes place in America on the last Thursday in November each year?

23 How did George Orwell arrive at the year 1984 for the setting of his classic novel?

24 Commonwealth Day had a different name before 1958. What was it?

25 Why were the dates 8 May and 14 August celebrated in many Western countries in 1995?

26 Tishri, Heshvan, Kisler, Tevet and Shevat are consecutive months in which calendar?

27 What is the name given to the attempt by army officers to assassinate Adolf Hitler in 1944?

28 How long, approximately, does it take for the Earth to revolve one complete turn on its own axis?

29 How many days' play are set aside by the TCCB for a cricket Test match: 2, 3, 4, 5, 6?

30 Topaz and chrysanthemum are the gemstone and flower associated with which month?

ABOUT TURN, LADS.

Answers on page 204

QUIZ NUMBER 4

Knowall's question:

What is the collective term for a group of whales?

A SHOAL !!!

1 The corruption of what German word for "lightning" is used to describe a dramatic play in American Football?

2 Which group of Caribbean islands shares its name with a species of South American alligator?

3 When a performer begins to *ad lib*, what has he or she started doing?

4 Which day of the week is dedicated to the Old English goddess of love?

5 If you went into a Japanese restaurant and asked for *sushi*, what would you be ordering?

6 What word can be used to describe either an elephant or a wide-bodied aeroplane?

7 What town gave its name to the fortified wine port, and in which country is it?

8 According to Cockney rhyming slang, what are you doing if you are "on the dog"?

9 What is both a soft fruit and a vulgar expression of disapproval?

10 Which French phrase means that something has been done and cannot be changed?

11 What is a "gazamia": an antelope, a football fan club, a herbaceous plant, a garden building?

12 Which unit of measurement specifies the distance a team of oxen could plough before needing a rest?

13 What word describes both the seat of government in Britain and three or more owls?

14 Why would a gourmet be more agreeable company than a gourmand at the dinner table?

15 Which item of household furniture is used to describe the head of a committee?

16 In various sports, which French term is used to denote the "Big Prize"?

17 What American phrase meaning goodbye derives from the Arabic word "salaam"?

18 Which duke popularised the waterproof knee-length boot that still bears his name?

19 In the latter and early parts of which two decades were people sometimes called baby-boomers born?

20 Which German word translates as "time-ghost" and is now used to allude to the spirit of an age?

21 What is a "toothsome" person fortunate to have in abundance?

22 What word meaning a strip or ring of pasta has also been used to describe a simpleton?

23 Henry II decreed that the distance from his nose to his thumb would represent which unit of measurement?

24 If you make a deal on the phone, is it construed as an oral or an aural contract?

25 What is a smörgåsbord and from which European country does it originate?

26 Who was "Peeping Tom the Tailor" gawping at when he was struck blind for his impudence?

27 Which comedian invented Cupid Stunt, who says "It's all done in the best *possible* taste"?

28 Which letter is used most frequently in the English language: a, e, i, s, t?

29 The name of which Italian amorist has become synonymous with overt sexual promiscuity?

30 What is the connection between a "ship's kitchen" and a "printer's proof"?

I CAN'T BELIEVE THEY EVER LET HIM OUT OF THE CLASSROOM.

Answers on page 204

Knowall's question:

What does the Latin expression *ad nauseam* mean?

TO INFINITY !!!

1 What are spring and neap tides respectively?

2 Why is an unmarried woman often called a "spinster"?

3 Who or what are the "grass roots" of an organisation?

4 Differentiate between the verbs "feint" and "faint"?

5 From what do the Romance languages derive?

6 Who would you address as "Your Grace"?

7 What is the opposite of enervating?

8 How are a group of lions collectively known?

9 What happens when someone "meets their Waterloo"?

10 Which cricket scores are called "Nelson"?

11 In rhyming slang, what does "taking a butcher's" mean?

12 How fast would you expect a viscous liquid to flow?

13 Fondue is a melted cheese dish from which country?

14 Where might you find Freshmen and Sophomores?

15 In the navy, what is a "dogwatch"?

16 What Spanish town is renowned for fine sword blades?

17 What does RSVP invite you to do?

18 Why might a bleb be irritating?

19 The zho is a cross between which two animals?

20 Which German word refers to a person's double?

21 "The Devil's picture book" is a puritan name for what?

22 What is Hobson's choice?

23 Nirvana is a state of spiritual bliss in which religion?

24 How is the humerus more popularly known?

25 What are the first three letters of the Greek alphabet?

26 In Italian sport, what is *Serie "A"*?

27 A "light-fingered person" is a euphemism for what?

28 What do you do if you apply the *coup de grâce*?

29 Agoraphobia is the fear of what?

30 What does a matador do for a living?

THIS IS REALLY STARTING TO MAKE ME SICK.

Answers on page 205

Knowall's question:

How many are there in a baker's dozen?

TWELVE !!!

1 A kleptomaniac cannot resist doing what?

2 What is a Molotov cocktail?

3 Why is Hamlet an "eponymous" hero?

4 What was a bashi-bazouk?

5 *Bambino* is an affectionate Italian word for what?

6 Whose catchphrase is "I've started so I'll finish"?

7 Which adjective means "fox-like"?

8 What do the French mean by *le piston*?

9 Literally translated, what is a Vespa?

10 What would be measured with an oometer?

11 Where is "Davy Jones' locker" found?

12 What is an Oedipus complex?

13 Which Latin phrase refers to an unwanted person?

14 Who or what was "Big Bertha"?

15 From whom was the brand name Nike derived?

16 What is a young hare called?

17 In rhyming slang, who is "trouble and strife"?

18 What is another word for "deadly nightshade"?

19 What is the common name of the disease variola?

20 Is "fustian" a type of vegetable, mould or cloth?

21 In wartime, who are Fifth Columnists?

22 Differentiate between "discrete" and "discreet"?

23 In what country are Magyars the predominant race?

24 What do Scots call the last day of the year?

25 What is a *faux-pas*?

26 What are so-called "white ants"?

27 What does *Schadenfreude* mean?

28 Soho is a London district and what else?

29 What is the collective noun for a group of bears?

30 How did Queen Elizabeth II describe the year 1992?

Answers on page 205

Knowall's question:

What is nicknamed "The Bill"?

A BIRD'S BEAK !!!

1 In World War 2, who was "The Forces' Sweetheart"?

2 What type of aircraft was first called a "jumbo jet"?

3 The US state of Florida is known as what?

4 What is a "Mae West"?

5 Which soldier and politician was "The Iron Duke"?

6 What type of natural phenomenon is "Old Faithful"?

7 Which (German) field marshal was "The Desert Fox"?

8 What newspaper is called "The Thunderer"?

9 Which snooker player is known as "Hurricane"?

10 By what nickname is a British private soldier known?

11 What flag is popularly described as "Old Glory"?

12 Which British actress was "The Jersey Lily"?

13 The Jaguar car is popularly called what?

14 Which British prime minister was "The Grocer"?

15 What is "The Old Lady of Threadneedle Street"?

16 What beast is known as "The King of the Jungle"?

17 Name the sinister Russian known as "The Mad Monk".

18 Which island is described as "The Emerald Isle"?

19 What was the nickname of 1960s athlete Mary Rand?

20 Who or what was "Puffing Billy"?

21 Which jazz great was nicknamed "Satchmo"?

22 What *exactly* is "Big Ben"?

23 What is the popular nickname of gin?

24 Which famous Victorian was "The Lady of the Lamp"?

25 Automotively, what is a "Green Goddess"?

26 The nickname of the camel is what?

27 What is eagerly described as "black gold"?

28 Which England fast bowler was called "Typhoon"?

29 What is "The Big Apple"?

30 In golf, who is "The Great White Shark"?

HE SHOULD BE ARRESTED.

Answers on page 205

QUIZ NUMBER 8

1 Who became the first Duke of Wellington shortly before ending Napoleon's comeback at Waterloo?

2 What unusual fact links the 19th-century writers George Eliot and George Sand?

3 What name launched a successful 1970s music career between Steven Georgiu and Yusuf Islam?

4 Which aristocrat, who laid down a set of rules for boxing, began life as simple John Douglas?

5 What oriental *nom de plume* did prolific short story writer Hector Hugh Munro use?

6 The Rev. Charles L. Dodgson was inspired by Alice Liddell to become which famous children's writer?

7 "No-name" Maddox took another, less enigmatic, name and became which notorious mass killer?

8 Pablo Ruiz adopted his mother's maiden name to become which famous 20th century painter?

9 What were the strange names taken by Irish rock performers Paul Hewson and Dave Evans.

10 Which best-selling American author specialising in raunchy novels had the given name Francis Kane?

11 Who became the Irish spinning-maid Betty Burke in a successful attempt to escape English troops?

12 By what name did public schoolboys know that keystone of Latin, Publius Vergilius Maro.

13 What sweet name was adopted by Walker Smith to take him on a spectacular boxing career from 1946?

14 Eric Arthur Blair, having adopted the name of a river in Suffolk, looked into the future in 1948. As whom?

15 Born Pauline Matthews, who helped Elton John to No. 1 in July 1976 with *Don't Go Breaking My Heart*.

16 Which famous comedy brothers' real names were Julius Henry, Adolph Arthur, Leonard and Herbert?

17 What animal-loving Italian who founded an order of monks was born Giovanni de Bernardone in 1181?

18 What singer called Henry John Deutschendorf Jnr replaced his surname with a city in the Rockies?

19 Which midget showman, made a "star" by P. T. Barnum, was born Charles Sherwood in Connecticut in 1838?

20 Which 16th-century Venetian painter used his father's trade (a dyer) for a name change from Jacopo Robusti?

21 What dictator preferred a name meaning "man of steel" to his given name of Josef Vissarionovich Dzhugashvili?

22 Letters from the famous to Willie Donaldson caused hilarity in the 1980s. To whom were they addressed?

23 Wild West "kid" Henry Longbaugh took his name from which Wyoming town where he was once jailed?

24 Which radio DJ and television comedian who died of Aids began life as Maurice Hope?

25 What Catholic peer, renowned for supporting dubious criminals, started out as plain Frank Pakenham?

26 She was born Anna Mary Robertson in 1861, had her first exhibition in 1940 and died aged 101. Who was she?

27 Born Arnold Dorsey, he was Gerry Dorsey before taking the snappy name of which minor German composer?

28 Which Hollywood actor combined Gibraltar and New York's river to come up with his successful name?

29 As Emily Lyon, born in 1765, who set out to find fame and became the mistress of a famous sailor?

30 Saigon would have been Nguyen That Thanh City in 1975 if which leader hadn't changed his name?

HIS CAREER'S ON THE SLIDE.

Answers on page 205

Knowall's question:

Who said "I have nothing to declare but my genius."?

ME, I DID !!!

1 "A horse! A horse! My kingdom for a horse!"

2 "A week is a long time in politics."

3 "God is really just another artist."

4 "Houston. Tranquility Base here. The Eagle has landed."

5 "One is not born a woman, one becomes one."

6 "I'm just going outside and may be some time."

7 "Let them eat cake."

8 "Float like a butterfly, sting like a bee."

9 "We have become a grandmother."

10 "To betray, you must first belong."

11 "Remember that time is money."

12 "I believe it is peace in our time."

13 "Ballads and babies. That's what happened to me."

14 "There can be no whitewash at the White House."

15 "When the going gets tough, the tough get going."

16 "The female of the species is more deadly than the male."

17 "Gentlemen, include me out."

18 "There's one step from the sublime to the ridiculous."

19 "We are not amused."

20 "More light!"

21 "Boxing's just show business with blood."

22 "I know nothing except the fact of my ignorance."

23 "He would, wouldn't he?"

24 "J'accuse!" (in a newspaper headline)

25 "The scouts' motto is founded on my initials."

26 "I have nothing to offer but blood, toil, tears and sweat."

27 "There's a sucker born every minute."

28 "It means the end of a thousand years of history."

29 "Bugger Bognor!"

30 "Early this morning I signed my death warrant."

THIS GUY CAN GET WILDLY OVER-ENTHUSIASTIC.

Answers on page 206

Knowall's question:

Who said "France has lost a battle, but France has not lost not the war."?

NAPOLEON !!!

1 "Doctor Livingstone, I presume?"

2 "This was their finest hour."

3 "Power is the ultimate aphrodisiac."

4 "Is Paris burning?"

5 "Big Brother is watching you."

6 "The sun is God."

7 "If you can't stand the heat, get out of the kitchen."

8 "I was a seven-stone weakling."

9 "We must love one another or die."

10 "Liberty is precious – so precious it must be rationed."

11 "I have made love to 10,000 women."

12 "Goodnight my darlings."

13 "All reactionaries are paper tigers."

14 "I cry all the way to the bank."

15 "I've got his pecker in my pocket."

16 "Mozart!"

17 "History is more or less bunk."

18 "I have a dream . . ."

19 "Comment is free, but facts are sacred."

20 "The unacceptable face of capitalism."

21 "Don't let poor Nellie starve."

22 "The only thing we have to fear is fear itself."

23 "Any man who hates dogs and babies can't be all bad."

24 "We're more popular than Jesus now."

25 "Black is beautiful."

26 "You won the election, but I won the count."

27 "You CANNOT BE SERIOUS!"

28 "Most of our people never had it so good."

29 "So much to do, so little done."

30 "You ain't heard nothin' yet."

HE'S GENERALLY USELESS ON HISTORY.

Answers on page 206

Knowall's question:

Lord Byron was accused of having an affair with a famous lady. Who was she?

LADY EMMA HAMILTON !!!

1 Who sensationally disappeared in 1973 after the murder of family nanny Sandra Rivett in London?

2 In 1996, who won the Russian presidential election despite health worries?

3 In 1915, which British nurse was executed in Brussels by the Germans for helping British and French soldiers?

4 What was the main company owned by disgraced tycoon Robert Maxwell at the time of his death?

5 Which flamboyant rock star member of Queen died of Aids in 1991?

6 Whose long-time friendship with model Gennifer Flowers threatened his political ambitions in 1992?

7 After World War 1, which British PM became embroiled in an "honours for cash" row?

8 In 1989, which British tourist was murdered in a Kenya game park, though the authorities blamed wild animals?

9 In 1915, which young British poet died of blood poisoning following a mosquito bite?

10 Who was America's "King of Junk Bonds", sentenced to 10 years for violating federal laws in 1990?

11 Which unconventional American dancer's two children were drowned in a 1913 Paris motoring accident?

12 Who ordered the *fatwa* on author Salman Rushdie after his book *The Satanic Verses* was published?

13 Members of which country's football team were accused of vandalising an airliner in 1996?

14 New Yorker Katie Mulcahey was the first victim of a 1908 law banning women from doing what in public?

15 Which world statesman's wife was sentenced to prison for kidnapping and beating young men?

16 Whose missed putt on the final green at Kiawah Island in 1991 cost Europe the Ryder Cup?

17 Which famous Mexican revolutionary captured the town of Juárez in November 1913?

18 In 1981, which aristocrat's conviction for murdering his wife Sunny was overturned in America?

19 How was Tory MP William Huskisson sensationally killed in September 1830?

20 The British government tried to ban what book by ex-MI5 agent Peter Wright in 1988?

21 In 1906, which great Italian tenor was fined $10 for sexual harassment in New York?

22 Who resigned as the Grand Master of British Freemasons in February 1901?

23 Which waspish writer's diary was published in the 1950s with "names omitted to protect the guilty"?

24 In 1995, England rugby captain Will Carling's friendship with whom caused a public rift in his marriage?

25 Hitler altered his book title *Four and a Half Years of Struggle against Lies, Stupidity and Cowardice* to what?

26 Which American hotel queen was jailed for tax fraud after saying "only the little people pay taxes"?

27 In 1907 Jamaica governor Sir A. Sweetenham resigned after mismanaging what natural disaster?

28 Name the fallen Australian entrepreneur convicted in 1996 of fraud involving expensive modern paintings.

29 In 1941, which baronet was acquitted of murdering his wife Diana's lover Lord Errol in Kenya?

30 Which former East German leader fled to Chile after his trial for manslaughter collapsed in 1993?

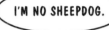

Answers on page 206

Knowall's question:

Which major politician *didn't* resign his senior position in 1992 after admitting an affair with his secretary?

CECIL PARKINSON !!!

1 Who was president when Colonel Oliver North diverted secret funds to the Nicaraguan Contras?

2 Whose assassination in Sarajevo provided the spark that ignited World War 1 in 1914?

3 In 1991, hardline Russian Communists deposed which president in a dawn coup?

4 Name the Austrian president who was engulfed in a storm over his Nazi past in 1988.

5 Which chancellor of the exchequer angrily resigned from Margaret Thatcher's government in 1989?

6 Who did America's CIA once plan to assassinate with an exploding cigar?

7 Which American boxing champion lost his title in 1967 for refusing to be drafted on religious grounds?

8 Name the Italian media tycoon who became prime minister before inevitable scandals brought him down.

9 Which flamboyant bohemian Welsh poet died young of alcohol poisoning in 1953?

10 Which so-called "Minister for Fun" resigned in 1992 when an affair with Antonia de Sancha became public?

11 Name the England cricket team manager fined £2,000 in 1996, though the penalty was overturned on appeal.

12 Which American silent movie comic's career nose-dived after he was acquitted of manslaughter in 1921?

13 In 1975, Judith Campbell Exner publicly revealed details of her affair with which American president?

14 Footballer Danny Blanchflower very publicly refused to participate in which TV show?

15 In the 1889 Mayerling Affair, the heir of Emperor Franz Joseph killed his lover and shot himself. Who was he?

16 What failed political party was folded by its leader David Owen in 1990?

17 Which singer quit a world concert tour in 1993 to seek treatment for addiction to painkillers?

18 The Duchess of York's father was sensationally accused of visiting a Soho massage parlour in 1985. Name him.

19 Who wrote *Mrs Warren's Profession*, a play closed by New York police in 1905 for indecency?

20 Which respected economist predicted disaster after analysing the 1919 Treaty of Versailles?

21 A member of 1970s pop duo T. Rex died in a 1977 car crash. Who was he?

22 Who led a 1984 strike against pit closures which failed amid violent confrontation between miners and police?

23 In 1991, the case against directors of which firm failed despite government efforts to withhold vital evidence?

24 Which American folk singer had a long-running but spasmodic relationship with Bob Dylan?

25 Which bloodthirsty president terrorised Uganda for eight years before fleeing to Saudi Arabia?

26 What was PM Harold Wilson's resignation honours list, said to be compiled by Lady Falkender called?

27 Which actress mistress of the Prince of Wales took out American citizenship in 1900?

28 Whose special envoy was Terry Waite, released after five years as a hostage in Lebanon?

29 Which notorious architect was imprisoned in 1974 for corruption in local government contracts?

30 In 1990, what fate befell Iranian-born British *Observer* journalist Farzad Bazoft in Iraq?

Answers on page 207

Knowall's question:

Who resigned in 1990 after saying of loss of sovereignty to Europe: "You might as well hand it to Hitler."?

MARGARET !!!

1 In 1990, which agriculture minister fed hamburgers to his daughter to show there was no threat from BSE?

2 Which prominent suffragette leader was sent to prison in 1908 for obstructing the police outside parliament?

3 With whose party was Major Hugh Lindsay when he was killed skiing off-piste at Klosters in 1988?

4 In 1994, defence chief Sir Peter Harding resigned after an affair with whom became public?

5 Which American president suffered "a complete nervous breakdown" in 1919?

6 Who was the manager of the Manchester United team decimated by the Munich air crash in 1958?

7 Which Rolling Stone was sacked in 1969 and later died tragically in his swimming pool?

8 The name of which Norwegian shot in 1945 for Nazi collaboration has become synonymous with treason?

9 Whose activities in 1950s London caused his name to enter the language as a byword for ruthless landlords?

10 Which sculptor outraged Paris in 1901 with his semi-nude reclining figure of national icon Victor Hugo?

11 Which German terrorist co-founder of the Red Army Faction committed suicide in her prison cell in 1976?

12 Name the American former jailbird and political activist murdered by rival Black Muslims in 1965.

13 In 1898, which American press baron promoted war with Spain to boost circulation of his *New York World*?

14 Which notorious Venezuelan terrorist masterminded the kidnap of OPEC oil ministers in 1975?

15 Name the leading British jockey imprisoned in 1987 for a major tax fraud.

16 Oscar Wilde's downfall began when he sued which aristocrat, father of his friend Lord Alfred Douglas?

17 Which birth control pioneer won a libel action against a doctor who accused her of encouraging immorality?

18 Which former chairman of Guinness was jailed in 1990 for illegally supporting the company's shares?

19 Murderer Dr Crippen and his mistress Ethel Le Neve were the first criminals to be caught in what way?

20 Name the Australian premier sacked by the governor-general in 1975 amid furious controversy.

21 A judge called which Scientology cult leader a "pathological liar gripped by avarice and a lust for power"?

22 American anarchist Emma Goldman was arrested in 1901 for plotting to assassinate which president?

23 Which leader of the Liberal Party resigned after being acquitted of conspiring to murder Norman Scott?

24 In 1991, which volatile Italian-based Argentinian soccer star was banned for drug-taking?

25 Which film director created *Olympiad*, a dramatic celebration of the 1936 Olympics and Nazi ideology?

26 New York's Metropolitan Opera House banned *Salome* as obscene in 1906. Who composed the opera?

27 In 1987, who was discredited when photographed with model Donna Rice on the yacht *Monkey Business*?

28 Which Egyptian president was assassinated at a military parade by Muslim fundamentalists in 1981?

29 In 1989, which top Rumanian gymnast sought political asylum in Hungary?

30 What ruling Italian political party was destroyed by massive corruption scandals in the early 1990s?

HE'LL NEVER SOLVE THAT RIDDLE.

Answers on page 207

Knowall's question:

Spot the odd one out: brain, heart, kidneys, liver, pancreas, scapula, spleen.

BRAIN !!!

1 Inch, foot, yard, chain, furlong, acre, mile.

2 Plantagenet, Tudor, Stuart, Bourbon, Hanover.

3 Midshipman, pilot officer, sub-lieutenant, commander.

4 Crimplene, cotton, nylon, polyester, rayon, terylene.

5 Diana, Mercury, Minerva, Neptune, Vulcan, Zeus.

6 Drachma, dollar, franc, guilder, petra.

7 Cheetah, hyena, leopard, jaguar, panther, puma.

8 Ballet, foxtrot, quickstep, samba, tango, waltz.

9 King, prince, duke, count, earl, viscount, baronet.

10 Anglican, Baptist, Buddhist, Catholic, Methodist.

11 Cabbage, cauliflower, marrow, spinach, tomato.

12 Bach, Beethoven, Brahms, Braque, Bruckner.

13 Mars, Mercury, Jupiter, Neptune, Orion, Saturn.

14 Brandy, gin, sherry, tequila, vodka, whisky.

15 Bears, Bulls, Cowboys, Dolphins, Giants, Steelers.

16 Bombay, Cape Town, Milan, New York, Paris, St Petersburg, Shanghai, Sydney, Rio de Janeiro.

17 *Gigi, The King and I, Oklahoma!, The Sound of Music, South Pacific.*

18 Indira Gandhi, John F. Kennedy, Pol Pot, Yitzhak Rabin, Anwar Sadat, Leon Trotsky, Henrik Verwoerd.

19 *You Really Got Me, Tired of Waiting For You, Sunny Afternoon, Waterloo Sunset.*

20 Basilisk, centaur, griffin, harpy, minotaur, phoenix, satyr, tigon.

21 Beethoven, Jorge Luis Borges, Ray Charles, George III, Homer, John Milton, Stevie Wonder.

22 Apache, Blackfoot, Cheyenne, Cree, Huron, Iroquois, Montana, Navajo, Pawnee, Sioux.

23 Buddy Holly, Sanjay Gandhi, Yuri Gagarin, Graham Hill, Grace Kelly, Rocky Marciano, Otis Redding.

24 Arsenal, Chelsea, Crystal Palace, Everton, Queen's Park Rangers, Tottenham Hotspur, West Ham United.

25 *The Gondoliers, Iolanthe, HMS Pinafore, The Merry Widow, The Mikado, The Pirates of Penzance.*

26 Chutney, dungarees, jodhpurs, pyjamas, shampoo, taboo, verandah.

27 Honor Blackman, Joanna Lumley, Helen Mirren, Diana Rigg, Linda Thorson.

28 *Flying Scotsman, Golden Arrow, Great Eastern, Orient Express, Trans-Siberian Express.*

29 Aria, concerto, overture, prelude, quintet, serenade, sonata, symphony.

30 Brachiosaurus, brontosaurus, mammoth, pterodactyl, triceratops, tyrannosaurus.

THAT WAS A HARD ONE.

Answers on page 207

QUIZ NUMBER 15

Knowall's question:

What liquid is produced by the lacrymal glands?

SALIVA !!!

EASY

1   About what age do men stop growing: 17, 19, 21 or 23?

2   What is the function of an artery?

3   Which area of physiology is studied by a cytologist?

4   What is the only muscle not attached at both ends?

5   If we breathe in oxygen, what do we breathe out?

6   How many layers of skin do you have: 1, 3, 5 or 7?

7   What is the name of the "soft spot" on a baby's head?

8   Which organs filter the water in your body?

9   What unwanted "extra" causes Down's Syndrome?

10   What is the proper term for the "Adam's apple"?

11   Where are your stirrup, hammer and anvil located?

12   The colon is the anatomical term for what?

13   What does the gall bladder store: bile, blood or urine?

14   Which part of the body does Hodgkin's Disease affect?

15   Rickets is caused by lack of sunlight and what vitamin?

16 What is the natural oil secreted by the skin called?

17 Name one of the two female sex hormones.

18 What is the "sheath" from which a hair grows?

19 Ossification is the process of forming what substance?

20 What is melanin?

21 The cornea is the protective shield for what organ?

22 During a hysterectomy, what is removed?

23 How many chambers are there in the human heart?

24 What disease is dangerous for babies in pregnancy?

25 Which part of the body is most sensitive to touch?

26 What is the hardest substance in the human body?

27 Diabetes is caused by a deficiency of what?

28 What is the common terms for dysmenorrhoea?

29 Which nerve connects the eyes to the brain?

30 Diazepam is better known to its consumers as what?

Answers on page 208

Knowall's question:

An adult human should have four of what type of tooth?

MOLARS !!!

1   Which is the largest gland in the human body: liver, lymph, pancreas or prostate?

2   Laudanum was once used to treat diarrhoea. What plant does it come from?

3   What is the difference between the "grey matter" and the "white matter" in the brain?

4   How long does it take for blood to circulate round the average body: 23, 53, 83, 113 or 143 seconds?

5   What gland, situated in the centre of the brain, is our "master gland", controlling many bodily activities?

6   Which two colours are most often confused by people suffering from colour blindness?

7   How many blood cells die every second in the body: 150, 1,500, 15,000, 150,000, 1.5 million, 15 million?

8   Which human blood group is missing: A, B, O, Rhesus negative, Rhesus positive?

9   What is the name given to the medical speciality of straightening and correcting teeth?

10 On average, there is only one age where girls are heavier and taller than boys: 10, 11, 12, 13 or 14?

11 How long is the small intestine: 1 metre (3ft 3in), 3 metres (10ft), 6 metres (20ft) or 10 metres (33ft)?

12 How long did the first heart transplant patient live: 3, 18, 32, 49 or 68 days?

13 Which part of the body suffers from the diseases of cirrhosis and hepatitis?

14 How much blood is in circulation at any one time: 2.5 lit (5.3 pints), 3.5 lit (7.4 pints), 4.5 lit (9.5 pints)?

15 The blood disease haemophilia is strange in that it affects only one section of the population. Who?

16 If you could separate the skin from an average man's body, how much would it weigh?

17 How many weeks does it take for a foetus to fully develop in the womb?

18 Roughly how many hairs do humans have on the head: 1,000, 10,000, 100,000, 1 million, 10 million?

19 The disease of scurvy, suffered by seaman until the 19th century, was caused by a lack of which vitamin?

20 By what shorthand is the hallucinogenic drug lysergic acid diethylmide better known?

21 Where in your body are your humerus, ulna, radius and carpals?

22 Which other type of food intake does a human require: carbohydrates, fats, proteins, vitamins, water?

23 What is the name for the smallest of the blood vessels in the body?

24 What two things can babies do at the same time that adults find impossible?

25 Why is a regular intake of calcium crucial as part of a healthy diet, especially in children?

26 The mandible is the only bone in the skull that can move independently. Which one is it?

27 What is the principal acid in the gastric juices that break down food in the stomach?

28 How many sperm does an average man produce each day: 50,000, 500,000, 5 million, 50 million, 500 million?

29 Nucleus, cell body, dentrites, axon, sheath and terminal are the parts of what?

30 Which women have more hairs on their head: blondes, brunettes or redheads?

IT'S A DOG'S LIFE.

Answers on page 208

Knowall's question:

Which is the most sensitive of the five human senses?

COMMON SENSE !!!

1 How many bones comprise the skull: 12, 17, 22 or 27?

2 What is the more common name for haemorrhoids?

3 On which part of the body do you get verrucas?

4 After strangulation, what bone is usually broken?

5 Alopecia is the medical name for what condition?

6 What is the name of the division between the nostrils?

7 Leukemia is caused by abnormalities in what?

8 What is the total "area" of the average man's skin?

9 What do we call the spaces within the facial bones?

10 Name the tubes that carry ova to the uterus.

11 What is the longest bone in the human body?

12 De-oxygenated blood is carried by which vessels?

13 What are you frightened of if you have mysophopia?

14 How many pairs of ribs do humans have?

15 What is the most common blood group?

16 What is the common name for the trachea?

17 Prosthetics is the making of what?

18 What is the primary function of the kidneys?

19 How many teeth comprise a "full" adult set?

20 Which is the biggest muscle in the human body?

21 What part of the body is affected by glaucoma?

22 Which bone in the body is most often broken?

23 Anaemia is caused by a deficiency of what?

24 What is the common term for acetylsalicylic acid?

25 Which of the seven vertebrae is the "lowest"?

26 What was the world's first effective antibiotic?

27 Skin, hair and nails all share which component?

28 What is the tendon at the top of the human heel?

29 The tibia is better known as what bone?

30 What part of the leg is an anagram of "elation"?

Answers on page 208

Knowall's question:

What sign of the zodiac covers September 24 to October 23?

VIRGO !!!

1 What was the ceaseless medieval search for a method of turning base metal to gold called?

2 Which Frenchman published *Centuries* in 1555, a book of rhyming prophesies up to the year 3797?

3 What pack of cards called "Arcana" can be used to predict the future?

4 Which mythical creature with human head and lion's body symbolised an Egyptian pharaoh's divinity?

5 Name the legendary Greek aviator who died when he flew too close to the Sun and wax in his wings melted.

6 Which terrifying Hindu goddess represents both love and destruction?

7 Which Anglo-Saxon warrior prince featured in an epic poem and died from a dragon's poisonous breath?

8 Mother Earth, daughter of the Great Spirit and Father Sky appear in the mythology of which native people?

9 What monastic order was disbanded in 1314 when its 22nd Grand Master was burned at the stake?

10 What ugly sisters of Greek mythology were immortal – except for Medusa, who was killed by Perseus?

11 Ferghus was an Irish hero of superhuman size and strength. Which kingdom did he rule?

12 Early explorers believed that a city of fabulous wealth existed in the interior of South America. Name it.

13 What society, often thought mysterious, was founded in 1717 with the Grand Lodge of London?

14 What name was given to the Roman goddess of fertility, hunting and the Moon?

15 In Norse mythology, the Gods of War had female helpers. What were they known as?

16 In the second century AD, Ptolemy established which mystic art that still thrives today?

17 Which Egyptian god associated with fertility later became Supreme God and King of the Underworld?

18 What legendary journey was undertaken to recover the Golden Fleece of Colchis?

19 What mythical warrior king of the Ancient Britons held court at Camelot?

20 Name the race of mounted women warriors from Scythia defeated by the Athenians around 500BC.

21 What Central American people worshipped the gods Xbalanque and Hunahpu?

22 According to legend, which great continent which was an earthly paradise sank into the sea and disappeared?

23 Which dark ceremony seeks to pervert the meaning of religion by worshipping the Devil instead of God?

24 Traditionally, the universe is made up of what four physical elements?

25 In the 19th century, what word did Charles Richet coin to describe the study of the paranormal?

26 Which black magician wrote *White Stains* and spent his life pursuing supernatural powers and sexual excess?

27 What multi-talented Roman God of the Sun was also responsible for music, poetry, prophesy and healing?

28 The Air Spirit, Sea Spirit and Moon Spirit are the three great spirit forces of which northern people?

29 In Egyptian mythology, Amun (also known as Ammon, Amen or Amon) was what?

30 What is the name of the Greek goddess associated with vengeance?

Answers on page 208

Knowall's question:

In what language was the New Testament originally written?

HEBREW !!!

1 According to legend, who rid Ireland of its snakes?

2 What is the supreme goal of Buddhists?

3 Who did the crowd want freed in preference to Jesus?

4 What does the word "rabbi" literally mean?

5 In the Christian calendar, what date is Epiphany?

6 What is the highest of the Hindu castes?

7 Which royal ruler put Daniel in the lion's den?

8 Who is the "supreme head of the Church of England"?

9 Which religious sect publishes *The Watch Tower*?

10 What is the name of the holy book of Islam?

11 Who exiled the Jews to Babylon in 586BC?

12 What does the abbreviation *FID DEF* stand for?

13 By what name do we know Siddarta Gautama?

14 Which architectural style preceded Perpendicular?

15 Which direction do Muslims face when they pray?

16 Which day is the Sabbath, the Jewish holy day?

17 What is the Sixth Commandment?

18 In which European country is the Pope's residence?

19 What is an Islamic edict (special command) called?

20 Genesis is the first book of the Bible. What's next?

21 Who was the holy cousin of Jesus?

22 What is the name of the Salvation Army's journal?

23 The founder of which religion spoke Aramaic?

24 What cruel Catholic "tribunal" was started in 1223?

25 Shinto is the main religion of which Asian country?

26 What was Matthew's job before he became a disciple?

27 How many "loaves and fishes" fed the 5,000?

28 Which city in the Punjab is the holy city of the Sikhs?

29 How many "books" are in the Bible: 56, 66, 76, 86, 96?

30 What is the last word in the New Testament?

Answers on page 209

Knowall's question:

In 1631 every copy of Robert Baker's new edition of the Bible was burnt and the printer was heavily fined. Why?

IT WAS IN LATIN !!!

1 The majority of the world's Muslims are Sunni. What is the other principal sect, most prominent in Iran?

2 Which outspoken MP formed the Free Presbyterian Church of Ulster in 1951?

3 What is the name of the ceremony when Jewish boys "come of age" at 13 years and one day?

4 What nationality are the papal police force, whose uniforms were designed by Michelangelo?

5 Why do Sikh men wear turbans on their heads and nets round their beards?

6 Which sect, prominent in Lebanon and led by Walid Jumblatt from 1977, draws on Christianity and Islam?

7 What, lamentably, comes next: Job, Psalms, Proverbs, Ecclesiastes, Song of Solomon, Isaiah, ...?

8 Which austere Christian sect holds that everyone has the power to communicate directly with God?

9 What is the name of the towers on mosques from which the *muezzin* call faithful Muslims to prayer?

10 In 1517, how many theses did Martin Luther nail to the door of Wittenberg Church: 15, 35, 55, 75, 95?

11 Which country's population has the highest proportion of Rastafarians?

12 What is the name of a state where the sole sovereign is God and priests rule on his behalf?

13 What mark of respect do Muslims earn if they have completed *Hajj*, the pilgrimage to Mecca?

14 Who is the patron saint of France, the first bishop of Paris who built a church on an island in the Seine?

15 What Catholic order, also called The Society of Jesus, was founded by Ignatius de Loyola in 1540?

16 By what name is the ancient Chinese philosopher K'ung Fu-tse ("Kong the Master") better known?

17 In which century was Joan of Arc made a saint: 16th, 17th, 18th, 19th, 20th?

18 What does "Singh" mean, one of many changes made to the Sikh religion by Govind Singh (1666-1708)?

19 Who was the translator of the first complete Bible printed in English in 1535?

20 In Hinduism, what is the law whereby consequences of actions in this life are carried over into the next?

21 What position in Poland did Pope John Paul II hold before being appointed pontiff in 1978?

22 The "five Ks" of Sikhdom are long hair, comb, shorts worn under clothes, a sabre-like knife and what else?

23 What was formerly called the Christian Revival Association and the East London Christian Mission?

24 In which century was Islam founded by Mohammed: 3rd, 5th, 7th, 9th, 11th?

25 In which country is the world's biggest cathedral: France, Italy, Ivory Coast, Russia, Spain, Vatican City?

26 Both Jews and Muslims are forbidden to eat the meat of which animal?

27 Who is the Archbishop of Cape Town who won the Nobel Peace Prize in 1984 for fighting apartheid?

28 What name is given to Jews living in Europe who conform rigidly to their religion's laws and conventions?

29 What is the town in south-west France where each year millions of pilgrims pray to be cured of illness?

30 In the St Bartholomew Massacre of 1572 over 25,000 Huguenots were slaughtered. Who were Huguenots?

THERE'S A THIRD PARTY INVOLVED AS WELL AS FIRE AND THEFT.

Answers on page 209

Knowall's question:

In 1611, who was cast adrift by his mutinous crew in northern waters?

CAPTAIN BLIGH !!!

1 Which battle marked the end of the Napoleonic Wars, and in what year did it take place?

2 In the mid-14th century, what killed around a third of Europe's population?

3 Which revolutionary Socialist died in 1883 and was buried in London's Highgate cemetery?

4 From where was the British Army evacuated ahead of the advancing Germans in 1940?

5 Who is reputed to have said "Veni, vidi, vici." ("I came, I saw, I conquered.")?

6 Which scheming cleric who died in 1661 virtually ruled France during the "minority" reign of King Louis XIV?

7 What previously unconquered Alpine peak was scaled by the British artist Edward Whymper in 1865?

8 Name the Venetian merchant who became a favourite of Mongol Emperor Kublai Khan in the 1280s.

9 Which Elizabethan seaman and privateer was executed in 1618 after an unsuccessful expedition to America?

10 What knightly order founded by Edward III in 1349 still exists today?

11 In what year was London's Great Exhibition of the world's art and commerce staged in Hyde Park?

12 Which feared invader from the east was forced to retreat in 451AD, after a fierce battle in Gaul?

13 On what day of what month in what year was the American Declaration of Independence made?

14 In 1894, which French officer later defended by Zola was convicted of treason and sent to Devil's Island?

15 What ship conveyed 120 anti-Catholic Puritans across the Atlantic in 1620?

16 During the French Revolution, who was stabbed to death in his bath by Charlotte Corday?

17 The great Arab city of Valencia was captured by which Christian commander in 1094?

18 Which ruthless land agent in 1870s Ireland was shunned by the local populace?

19 China's Communists broke through Chiang Kai-shek's encircling forces to begin what journey in 1934?

20 What surprise tactic was used to disrupt the Spanish Armada's attack on England in 1588?

21 What "first" was achieved by B-29 *Enola Gay* at the end of World War 2?

22 In 1845, which large republic became the 38th state of the United States?

23 The Battle of Trafalgar in 1805 saw the death of which famous commander?

24 In a battle in 61AD, the Romans killed 80,000 Britons commanded by which famous Celtic leader?

25 Name the two aviation pioneers who made the first non-stop Atlantic crossing in 1919.

26 Which European explorer was the first to sail around the Cape of Good Hope?

27 Who led the victorious Allied forces into Paris in August 1944?

28 In Germany, which Dutch refugee with a Latin name published the first serious map of the world in 1569?

29 What private security force defeated striking Pittsburgh steel workers in a pitched battle in 1892?

30 Who set out to design a new city after Rome was devastated by fire in 64AD?

MUCH MORE OF THIS AND I'LL BE BAYING FOR BLOOD.

Answers on page 209

Knowall's question:

In 1862, who landed in southern Italy with a view to unifying the country?

MUSSOLINI !!!

1 What was the first war in which the USA participated that it actually lost?

2 Whose ear, severed by Spanish coastguards in 1739, led to war between Britain and Spain?

3 After World War 2, where did the war crimes trials of leading Nazis take place?

4 Around 675BC, which city overtook Tyre as the main centre of Phoenician civilisation?

5 Which new framework for French law was finally approved in 1804?

6 Which two great writers, one English and one Spanish, died within two days of each other in April 1616?

7 What extraordinary event on 20 September 1378 split the Roman Catholic Church?

8 China's imperial capital of Beijing was captured by whose Mongol army in 1215?

9 What monument symbolising the friendship between France and the USA was dedicated in 1886?

10 Where was General "Chinese" Gordon killed by the Mahdi's Dervish army in January 1885?

11 Which spiritual leader fled his country on 25 December 1950 following a Chinese invasion?

12 In 1862, John King was the only survivor of a three-man team that set out to cross Australia. Who died?

13 What German city was largely destroyed by a fire-storm after intense bombing in February 1945?

14 In 1566, the revered emperor who had ruled the Ottoman Empire for 46 years died. Name him.

15 Following Lenin's death, who was ousted by Stalin from the leadership of the Soviet Communist Party?

16 What shocking event followed King Henry II's angry remark "who will free me from this turbulent priest?"?

17 Which event destined to have a shattering effect on the world took place on 29 October 1929?

18 At the start of World War 1, what were commandeered from Paris to rush troops to the front?

19 Which great English sailor was buried at sea off Panama in a lead coffin?

20 In the 1790s, which young Scottish explorer was the first European to penetrate the West African interior?

21 Which Indian leader was assassinated in Tamil Nadu on 24 May 1991?

22 George III appointed a sickly 24-year-old as Britain's prime minister in 1783. Who was he?

23 Which English king died in 1199 after being hit in the shoulder by a crossbow bolt?

24 What ocean liner was sunk by a German submarine with massive loss of life off Ireland in May 1915?

25 Around 600BC, who set out to turn Babylon into the world's greatest city?

26 What major sea battle between Christians and Turks took place in 1571?

27 In what year does China regain full sovereignty over the Portuguese territory of Macau?

28 The Volstead Act passed in the USA in 1919 aimed to stop what?

29 What was used to give William the Conqueror an inventory of his new kingdom in the 1080s?

30 Which famous Australian outlaw executed in 1880 wore armour made from metal plate?

THAT ANSWER REALLY TAKES THE BISCUIT.

Answers on page 209

Knowall's question:

In 494BC, Patrician rulers of Rome were challenged by Roman commoners called what?

LEGIONNAIRES !!!

1 Where – and in what year – did the invading Normans defeat England's King Harold?

2 Then the world's tallest man-made structure, what was opened in 1889?

3 What document was sealed at Runnymede, on the River Thames, in June 1215?

4 In what year did the Berlin Wall come down, marking the unexpectedly rapid end of the Cold War?

5 Which renegade gladiator led a slave revolt against the Roman Empire in 71BC?

6 To which Moroccan port did Kaiser Wilhelm II despatch a German gunboat in 1911?

7 Who succeeded Konstantin Chernenko as Soviet leader in 1985?

8 Which monarch was on the throne when England and Scotland were joined by the Act of Union in 1707?

9 Name the great Irish leader who died at the Battle of Clontarf in 1014.

10 In 1904 a surprise naval attack at Port Arthur signalled the start of war between which two countries?

11 Which Central American state was invaded by US Marines in December 1989?

12 What 12-year economic "siege" in southern Europe ended in 1982 when Britain promised talks?

13 Which Persian mathematician, astrologer and poet is best remembered for his *Rubaiyat*?

14 Name the Argentinian president deposed after his country lost the Falklands War.

15 Which great leader renowned for his thoughts died on 9 September 1976, aged 82?

16 Which Eastern European dictator was executed by firing squad on Christmas Day in 1989?

17 What, in 1807, did Britain abolish after a prolonged campaign by William Wilberforce?

18 Which great campaigner for Indian independence first became politically active in South Africa?

19 The Battle of Sedan in 1870 was the first major engagement of which European war?

20 Which former dissident playwright became president of Czechoslovakia in 1989?

21 Which deposed prime minister of Pakistan was hanged for treason in 1979?

22 Who treacherously defeated Inca King Atahualpa at Cajamarca, Peru in 1532?

23 In what year did failed assassination attempts on both President Reagan and the Pope take place?

24 The building of what, wrongly said to be the only man-made structure visible from space, began in 287BC?

25 What union destined to play a key role in Poland's fight for democracy was founded in September 1980?

26 Speculative trading mania involving which horticultural item engulfed Holland in the 1630s?

27 In 330AD, the centre of the Roman Empire ceased to be Rome itself. What was the new capital city?

28 Whose forces were defeated by English troops at the Battle of Culloden in 1746?

29 In what year did America's Great California Gold Rush take place?

30 Of which modern war did "Operation Desert Storm" mark the climax?

THERE'S A PLEBBY ANSWER FOR YOU.

Answers on page 210

Knowall's question:

Whose funeral was seriously disrupted by flooding of Bath Road, Maidenhead in 1852?

PRINCE ALBERT'S !!!

1 In what century did the Houses of Lancaster and York fight the Wars of the Roses?

2 Which Scottish MP was leader of the Liberal Party from 1957 to 1967?

3 Name the foreign monarch who appeared on English coinage in the year 1555.

4 In 1992, what once-influential humorous political magazine folded after 150 years?

5 What was the approximate population of the British Empire in 1900: 100, 200, 300 or 400 million?

6 Which king reigned for 10 years but spent only a few months of that time in England?

7 A row about which helicopter firm led to ministerial resignations by Michael Heseltine and Leon Brittan?

8 Who was the first Labour prime minister to rule Britain with a majority in the House of Commons?

9 What was the army rank of Mark Phillips when he married Princess Anne in 1973?

10 What order did Charles 1 make with regard to the manufacture of paper?

11 Which king wrote farming articles using the pen-name Ralph Robinson?

12 What Berkshire air base was the scene of a long-running protest against Cruise missiles?

13 Henry VII's eldest son Prince Arthur was the first husband of which future wife of Henry VIII?

14 In 1993, what did Queen Elizabeth II agree to pay for the first time?

15 Of what European state was King George I the ruler before he ascended the throne of England in 1714?

16 For what purpose was bronze from cannons captured at the Battle of Sebastopol used until 1942?

17 In the 17th century, which Irish adventurer was pardoned after stealing some of the Crown Jewels?

18 What did John Major and Albert Reynolds sign hopefully at Downing Street in December 1993?

19 What name is given to the official usher of the House of Lords?

20 Who was the last British king to lead his troops on the field of battle?

21 In 1984, what did Prince Charles call: "A monstrous carbuncle on the face of a much-loved friend."?

22 Who died at Rouen in France after being thrown against the pommel of his horse's saddle?

23 What was the first English newspaper to reach a daily sale of one million copies?

24 Which chancellor of the exchequer did John Major dismiss and replace with Kenneth Clarke?

25 Who was appointed Viceroy of India in 1946, with a brief to oversee orderly progress to independence?

26 In English history, what name is used to describe the period from 1810 to 1820?

27 Which British prime minister renounced an earldom in order to take up the premiership?

28 For how long was Mary, Queen of Scots a prisoner in England: 4 years, 9 years, 14 years, 19 years?

29 What war finally ended with the recapture of Port Stanley by British troops?

30 Which one of Henry VIII's six wives survived to become his widow?

Answers on page 210

Knowall's question:

What "science of human devilry" did Oliver Cromwell indulge in at his daughter's wedding?

KISSING THE BRIDE!!!

1 The last battle on British soil saw the Young Pretender defeated by the Duke of Cumberland. Where?

2 Of which prime minister was it said: "He could not see a belt without hitting below it."?

3 What name was shared by the only two British kings never to be crowned?

4 Name the evangelist mainly responsible for bringing the Protestant faith to Scotland.

5 Where was the main focal point of Dublin's 1916 Easter Rising against British rule?

6 Who was the first female chief to run one of Britain's security services?

7 What changed hands for the last time in battle at Bosworth Field in 1485?

8 Robert Maxwell drowned in 1991 after vanishing from what yacht named after a daughter?

9 What type of biscuit is named after Queen Victoria's holiday home on the Isle of Wight?

10 Son of Edward III, father of Henry IV, uncle of Richard II. Who was he?

11 What new force was formed in 1908 by merging the Yeomanry and the Volunteers?

12 At which Welsh castle did the investiture of the Prince of Wales take place in 1969?

13 Down which river did the frigate HMS *Amethyst* make a daring dash for freedom in July 1949?

14 Following the Restoration, where was Charles II actually crowned as king?

15 Who claimed to be King Richard IV and was then imprisoned by Henry VII?

16 In 1967, which stricken oil tanker was bombed by the RAF in an attempt to head off major pollution?

17 What was the last word spoken by Charles I on the scaffold before his execution?

18 Which medieval Chancellor lifted his daughter's nightgown to show her off to a prospective husband?

19 When did the BBC launch the Third Programme, to be devoted to cultural broadcasts: 1938, 1946, 1951, 1956?

20 In 1906, what was the most northerly African country in the British Empire?

21 Which queen was tutored by Roger Ascham, who wrote more fluently in Greek than in English?

22 What were built along the south and east coasts in 1805 and 1806 to guard against French invasion?

23 Which major war ended with a surrender signed in a railway carriage in the Forest of Compiegne?

24 Where were three members of an IRA active service unit killed by the SAS in March 1987?

25 At which battle off Denmark did Admiral Horatio Nelson turn his blind eye to a signal?

26 How did George II reputedly sustain the injuries from which he died?

27 In 1900 which British royal was unhurt when an anarchist fired two shots at him at Brussels railway station?

28 What measurement was defined when Henry III laid three barleycorns in a line?

29 What was opened to the public for the first time in 1993 to help with rebuilding costs at Windsor Castle?

30 In 1820, who was the last queen of England to be formally tried for adultery?

TRUST HIM TO STEP OUT OF LINE.

Answers on page 210

QUIZ NUMBER 26

Knowall's question:

Which king once owned the *Kensington & Chelsea Post* newspaper?

KING RUPERT !!!

1 According to legend, which English king carelessly burned the cakes?

2 Which treaty designed to reshape Europe's economic future came into effect in November 1993?

3 Who became prime minister in 1976 after Harold Wilson's surprise resignation?

4 Which dramatist was a convicted murderer, military champion and in receipt of a royal pension?

5 What did Richard II once pawn because he was so short of funds?

6 The Queen missed the Epsom Derby for the first time in June 1984. Where was she instead?

7 What so-called "war" broke out between Britain and Iceland in 1958 and again in 1975?

8 Which prince conceived and planned Britain's Great Exhibition of 1851?

9 What dramatic event effectively paralysed Britain from 5 May 1926?

10 In 1993, who made the shock announcement that she was drastically curtailing her high-profile public life?

11 Against which king was the infamous Gunpowder Plot of 1605 directed?

12 Wilton House near Salisbury achieved what notable "first" in 1776?

13 Which British colony made a unilateral declaration of independence from Britain in 1965?

14 Politician and prime minister Neville Chamberlain originally came from which English city?

15 The effigies of which two legendary giants stand in the City of London's Guildhall?

16 Protestant Britain lost 11 full days when it finally adopted what in 1752?

17 The "Guildford Four" and the "Birmingham Six" were wrongly imprisoned for what crime?

18 To the nearest six months, for how long did the longest 20th-century British Parliament sit?

19 How many convicts were deported to Australia from Britain: 65,000, 98,000, 121,000, 137,000?

20 The first public supply of what utility was obtained from Surrey's River Wey in 1881?

21 Which determined prime minister said: "I am not prepared to stagger from crisis to crisis."?

22 What was the blood relationship between the kings Charles II and James II?

23 In 1965, who became the first grammar school boy to lead the Conservative Party?

24 Who was the first British monarch to visit America: George IV, Victoria, Edward VIII or George VI?

25 To what position was James Ramsay MacDonald elected in February 1911?

26 Which famous Quaker pointedly kept his hat on when he met Charles II?

27 In 1990 there was a major riot in London as angry protesters demonstrated against what unpopular tax?

28 In the single year of 1936, which three monarchs officially ruled the United Kingdom?

29 Which wife did Henry VIII insultingly describe as the "Flanders Mare"?

30 Which palace is the Queen's residence when she is officially in Scotland?

IT CERTAINLY WASN'T ENVER HOXHA.

Answers on page 210

Knowall's question:

Who was Dwight D. Eisenhower's running mate in the 1952 presidential election?

MAMIE EISENHOWER !!!

1 Which world champion heavyweight boxer received a six-year jail sentence for rape in 1992?

2 Members of what cross-burning racist secret society wear white robes with pointed hoods?

3 In what country was "discoverer of America" Christopher Columbus born?

4 What elite fighting force was created by the United States Congress in 1798?

5 What did the Dutch purchase from Canarsee Indians in 1626 for trade goods worth 60 guilders?

6 Which famous outlaw robbed his first train at Adair, Iowa in July 1873?

7 What hideous disease was brought back to Europe from the Americas in the 1520s?

8 In November 1864 which Confederate city was burned by General William T. Sherman?

9 Name the newspaper tycoon who died in 1917 leaving funds for annual awards to writers and journalists.

10 What was the first commodity to be taxed by Britain in 1764, causing friction with North American colonists?

11 Settlers from what area of Europe introduced the log cabin to North America in the early 1600s?

12 Name one of the two Indian chiefs whose forces killed General Custer at the Battle of Little Big Horn.

13 Which future statesman became the official surveyor of Culpeper County, Virginia in July 1749?

14 In 1898, Cuba was the flashpoint for war between the United States and which European country?

15 What significant "first" was achieved by Virginia Dare on 18 August 1587?

16 Name three of the four US presidents featured on the giant Mount Rushmore memorial in South Dakota.

17 By what nickname was the World War 2 Boeing B-17 bomber known?

18 Where in South Dakota were Sioux Indians slaughtered in 1890, marking the end of Indian resistance?

19 Which young newspaper owner retired in 1743 to pursue his scientific interests?

20 What did North American Plains Indians steal from Spaniards around 1600 to revolutionise their lives?

21 In 1901 America's "foremost Negro educator" was invited to the White House. Who was he?

22 Where did the Japanese bomb and seriously damage the US Pacific fleet on 7 December 1941?

23 In which state did the celebrated racial integration of Little Rock Central High School take place in 1957?

24 What did Walter Raleigh name the long stretch of coastline he claimed for England in 1584?

25 In 1974, which kidnapped American heiress helped her captors rob a bank?

26 Almost 13,000 Americans died in which war that ended in 1848?

27 Whose first commercially produced "family horse" was sold for $850 to a doctor in 1903?

28 Which 83-year-old transport tycoon died in 1877 leaving a massive $100 million fortune?

29 In 1607, who saved Captain John Smith from death near Jamestown, Virginia?

30 Name the president shot and killed by an anarchist at Buffalo, New York in 1901.

I SUPPOSE THAT IS A TRICKY ONE.

Answers on page 211

QUIZ NUMBER 28

Knowall's question:

In 1870, the Standard Oil Company was formed by which ruthless entrepreneur?

CARNEGIE !!!

1 Which San Antonio mission was taken by Mexican troops in 1836 with the loss of all 187 defenders?

2 Who was General-in-Chief of the Confederate forces in the American Civil War?

3 What significant document was finally approved on 17 September 1787?

4 In July 1934, J. Edgar Hoover's G-men killed which "Public Enemy No. 1" outside a Chicago cinema?

5 What college, founded in 1636, was renamed in honour of a new benefactor three years later?

6 Which notorious bearded pirate was killed off the coast of Virginia in 1718?

7 In 1883 the first pre-Murdoch "penny newspaper" was published in New York. What was it called?

8 Which president died of pneumonia just 31 days after his inauguration in 1841?

9 In what year did Columbus begin his second expedition to America: 1493, 1495, 1497, 1499?

10 Where did a CIA-sponsored invasion of Cuba fail disastrously in 1961?

11 In 1983 more than 200 US Marines were killed by a car bomb in which Middle East capital?

12 Who was arrested for polygamy on 2 October 1871 in Salt Lake City?

13 Which revered civil rights leader was murdered in Memphis on 4 April 1968?

14 For how many years did the American War of Independence actually last: 2, 4, 6, 8 or 10?

15 What was used to convene the Pennsylvania State Assembly for the first time in 1753?

16 Name the president elected in 1932 with the promise of a "New Deal" for America.

17 In October 1692, what notorious event took place at Salem, Massachusetts?

18 Who did actor John Wilkes Booth shoot and kill at the theatre on 15 April 1865?

19 Queen Victoria shook the hand of which legendary American markswoman in 1887?

20 In 1805 the Lewis and Clark expedition reached what geographical objective after an 18-month trek?

21 Name the infamous "lone assassin" alleged to have shot and killed President Kennedy.

22 Which senator from Wisconsin mounted a rabid 1950s crusade against Communist sympathisers?

23 The 1790 census recorded how many inhabitants of the USA: 1, 2, 3, 4 or 5 million?

24 The infant son of which famous American aviator was kidnapped and killed in 1932?

25 Which large bay discovered by Francis Drake in 1579 was initially known as "Drake's Bay"?

26 The United States Congress set what at 25 cents in June 1938?

27 In 1769, which backwoodsman first led a party through the Cumberland Gap in the Blue Ridge Mountains?

28 What legendary law enforcement agency was set up at Austin, Texas in 1857?

29 In 1892, on which New York island was a new immigration station opened?

30 When he visited Panama in 1906, which US president became the first to travel abroad while in office?

I'M AFRAID YOU'VE GOT THE WRONG FELLA.

Answers on page 211

Knowall's question:

Where exactly did the Great Fire of 1665 begin?

LONDON !!!

1. Where in Scotland was a PanAm Boeing 747 brought down by a bomb with the loss of 270 lives in 1988?

2. Over 120,000 people died in the tidal wave following the eruption of which volcano near Java in 1883?

3. What American city was devastated by earthquakes in 1868, 1906 and 1989?

4. Where did the worst disaster in civil aviation history happen, when two jumbo jets collided on the ground?

5. A bolt of lightning caused a disastrous conflagration at what great British building in July 1984?

6. When the *Titanic* sank on its maiden voyage in 1912, of which company was it the new flagship?

7. In 1935, what airship exploded and burned with the loss of 35 lives in New Jersey, USA?

8. What Soviet nuclear reactor "melted down" with severe environmental consequences in 1986?

9. At what English football club did a stand fire kill over 40 spectators in 1985?

10. A freak flood swept through which Devon village in the summer of 1952?

11. What happened to Korean Airlines Flight 007 and its 269 occupants in September 1983?

12. Which European capital city was largely destroyed by an earthquake in 1755?

13. What caused thousands to starve to death in the great Irish famine of 1845?

14. In 79AD, the volcano Vesuvius erupted and buried which resort town?

15. Which car ferry capsized off Zeebrugge in 1987 with massive loss of life?

16 What was the nickname of the Manchester United team, many of whom were killed in an air crash in 1958?

17 In 1966 an unstable coal tip slipped, killing 116 children and 28 adults in which Welsh village?

18 What caused the deaths of over 200 holidaymakers at a Spanish campsite in 1978?

19 Which inexorable old enemy wiped out more than 100,000 Londoners in 1664?

20 The disastrous North Sea oil-rig fire which took over 150 lives in 1988 swept through which platform?

21 In the 1980s, fans of Liverpool FC were involved in which two stadium tragedies?

22 Some 60 people lost their lives when the dredger *Bowbelle* struck which Thames pleasure craft in 1989?

23 In 1993, what siege ended in disaster when FBI agents stormed the Texas ranch of cult leader David Koresh?

24 Name the 1950s drug which produced the tragic side-effect of deformed babies when taken in pregnancy.

25 In 1988, a faulty signals system caused a train crash that killed 36 people near which London station?

26 What supertanker ran aground in Alaska's Prince William Sound, creating a massive pollution disaster?

27 Which hotel was damaged by an IRA bomb during the Tory Party Conference in October 1984?

28 In what year did the "Great Hurricane" lash Britain, killing 11 and blowing down millions of trees?

29 What natural disaster devastated the American Midwest in August 1993?

30 In 1545, Henry VIII's new flagship sank before his eyes with heavy loss of life. What was her name?

NOW THERE'S A SWEET AFTERSTHOUGHT.

Answers on page 211

Knowall's question:

The Whisky-A-Go-Go in Los Angeles was the world's first what?

COCKTAIL !!!

1 What is a theodolite?

2 The Manx cat lacks what distinguishing feature?

3 In computing terms, what is RAM?

4 What is the world's longest snake?

5 Who was burned as a heretic on 31 May 1431?

6 In which US state did Custer's Last Stand take place?

7 Which people undertook "The Great Trek" from 1835?

8 What percentage of votes is needed to elect a Pope?

9 Who was the first surgeon to use antiseptic?

10 What is the modern name of the Hellespont?

11 Which aviation "first" belongs to the Montgolfiers?

12 By what name is the "ordinary" bicycle better known?

13 How many players does a woman's lacrosse team have?

14 What is the normal temperature of the human body?

15 Who was known as "The Sun King"?

16 What is the literal translation of "Beelzebub"?

17 Name the Japanese art of miniature plant cultivation.

18 Which culinary delicacy is scientifically *Ascomycetes*?

19 Where did Napoleon go after the Battle of Waterloo?

20 In Japanese culture, what is *hari-kiri*?

21 Near what small harbour did the Light Brigade charge?

22 When was the United Kingdom formed?

23 What is significant about Louis Washkansky?

24 What is the world's oldest surviving republic?

25 Name the entrance to San Francisco Bay.

26 What is made from silica, soda and lime?

27 What German village holds a Passion play each decade?

28 Who was Lord Protector of the Commonwealth?

29 Where are the Heights of Abraham?

30 What kind of creature is a flying fox?

HE'S LEADING US A MERRY DANCE.

Answers on page 211

Knowall's question:

What is name of the Caribbean holiday island owned by Virgin bass Richard Branson?

JAMAICA !!!

1 In which country is the world's deepest known cave?

2 What sort of physical phenomenon is a tsunami?

3 What stretch of water separates Tasmania and Australia?

4 What is the popular American term for a tornado?

5 Vinson Massif is the highest point of which continent?

6 In which region is the wettest place in Britain?

7 What is a mesa?

8 After Greenland, what is the world's largest island?

9 How in terms of distance, does fog differ from mist?

10 Where is the group of rocks known as The Needles?

11 The Red Sea separates which two continents?

12 What is the world's second biggest desert?

13 Name the scale used for measuring wind speed.

14 What is a hurrricane called in the northern Pacific?

15 Name the longest river in Europe, all of it in Russia.

16 Which country is the biggest producer of uranium?

17 With glaciers, what can be lateral, medial or terminal?

18 The Kalahari Desert is in two countries. Name one.

19 What can be igneous, metamorphic or sedimentary?

20 What is the more common name for lignite?

21 Where does the cold Benguela Current flow?

22 What are the three main "ages" of a river?

23 Name the desert between Los Angeles and Las Vegas.

24 The technical name for "breakwaters" is what?

25 What mountains link the Black and Caspian seas?

26 Which is biggest: Europe, Australasia or Antarctica?

27 Where are the Aleutian Islands?

28 England's Peak District is composed of what rock?

29 What is the taiga?

30 Name the longest river in France.

Answers on page 212

QUIZ NUMBER 32

Knowall's question:

Shield cones, hornit cones and calderas are all shapes of what natural phenomenon?

ROCKS !!!

1 Which BBC TV weatherman gaffed in dismissing a viewer's claim of an impending hurricane in 1987?

2 What is the Arab word for a dry desert valley or gully that sometimes floods after sudden storms?

3 In terms of constant hot water, what do Iceland and New Zealand have in common?

4 What American volcano, in Washington state, lost about 400m (1,300ft) after erupting in 1980?

5 Normal, reverse, strike-slip, horst and graben are all types of what?

6 The Tibetans call it Chomolunga, meaning "Goddess Mother of the World". What is the English name?

7 Over 600,000 people died in the world's worst recorded earthquake at Tangshan, in 1976. Where is Tangshan?

8 What island was created by volcanic activity off the south coast of Iceland in 1963, soon rising to 150m (490ft)?

9 The Mammoth Cave National Park in the US is the world's most extensive cave system. In which state?

10 What comes next: crust, upper mantle, lower mantle, outer core, ...?

11 Which Scottish loch contains more water than all the lakes of England and Wales combined?

12 What is the theory stating that the main continents all began as one land-mass called Pangaea?

13 The North Atlantic Drift comes out of which powerful ocean current beginning off the east coast of the US?

14 What do ocean island nations such as the Maldives, Tuvalu and Kiribati fear from global warming?

15 The world's highest recorded wind speed is 191km/h (118.7mph), 251km/h (156mph) or 371km/h (231mph)?

16 Which famous waterfall in southern Africa is known locally as Mosi-oa-Toenja, "the smoke that thunders"?

17 Which volcanic mountain, Japan's highest and sacred to its people, has been dormant since 1707?

18 The Mercalli Scale measures an earthquake's effects at one place. What does the Richter Scale measure?

19 What was the position of Sir George Everest, after whom the world's highest mountain is named?

20 The British islands of Ascension, St Helena and Tristan da Cunha are located in which ocean?

21 Which geological fault system runs from the River Jordan and the Red Sea through Africa to Lake Nyasa?

22 The Mariana Trench, at 11,034m (36,200ft) the world's deepest known place, is in which ocean?

23 What is the heavy rainfall that arrives in southern and South-East Asia during the summer months?

24 Which country is by far the world's biggest producer of diamonds?

25 What is the name of the process that moves sand and shingle laterally along a beach?

26 The world's highest recorded shade temperature is 48°C (118.4°F), 58°C (136.4°F) or 68°C (154.4°F)?

27 What is the name of the mountain range that runs down almost the whole of western South America?

28 In Bangladesh, what caused over 300,000 deaths in 1970 and more than 200,000 deaths in 1991?

29 Which British river has an a wave-like bore that can reach 35km (22mi) upstream?

30 What is the name of the shrinking lake in Africa bordered by Nigeria, Niger, Chad and Cameroon?

IT MAKES YOU WANT TO ERUPT.

Answers on page 212

Knowall's question:

What island stretches east for 190km (120 miles) from the New York boroughs of Brooklyn and Queen's?

RHODE ISLAND !!!

1 What building's address is 1600 Pennsylvania Avenue, Washington D.C.?

2 Which of the Great Lakes is missing: Superior, Michigan, ..., Erie, Ontario?

3 In which state is Yellowstone, the oldest of the USA's national parks?

4 Which city is located at the confluence of the Missouri and Mississippi rivers?

5 Ottawa, the capital of Canada, is in which of the country's provinces?

6 Mt McKinley, the highest peak in North America, is in which US state?

7 Which American state was the 50th, and last, to join the Union in 1960?

8 The 1978 Commonwealth Games were held in which city, the capital of Alberta?

9 Which river flows through the Grand Canyon in Arizona?

10 What is the biggest state of the USA in terms of population?

11 What is the name of the waterway that connects the Great Lakes to the Atlantic Ocean?

12 The resort of Martha's Vineyard lies off the coast of which American state on the eastern seaboard?

13 What breed of dog was used to swim out with rope to boats and derives its name from an area of Canada?

14 Which grand river forms the US-Mexico border from El Paso in Texas to the Gulf of Mexico?

15 Greenland is a self-governing division of which European country?

16 Disneyland and Disney World are in which two American states?

17 A helicopter is named after a warm dry wind that blows over the Rockies. What is it?

18 O'Hare International Airport, fifth busiest in the United States, serves which "windy" city?

19 Canada has two "Great" lakes in the North-West Territories. Can you name one of them?

20 Which "new" state is missing: New Hampshire, New ...., New Mexico, New York?

21 The Bering Strait separates Alaska from which country in Asia?

22 From which Italian explorer does America, erroneously, derive its name?

23 In which American state is the presidential "retreat" of Camp David?

24 The USA and Canada are separated west of Ontario by which geographical parallel?

25 What is the French possession in the Atlantic Ocean south of Newfoundland?

26 In which Virginia town is the Pentagon, the HQ of the US Defense Department and military forces?

27 Name the world's fifth largest island, lying between Canada and Greenland.

28 Which city in Louisiana is famous for its annual Mardi Gras celebrations and jazz music?

29 What comes next: British Columbia, Alberta, Saskatchewan, Manitoba, Ontario, ...?

30 How much did the US pay Russia for Alaska in 1867: $7million, $70 million, $700 million, $7,000 million?

THE SHORT ANSWER ISN'T ALWAYS THE BEST.

Answers on page 212

Knowall's question:

What triggered the war between El Salvador and Honduras in 1969?

THE PRICE OF BANANAS !!!

1 Which mighty river of South America has seven tributaries more than 1,600km (1,000 miles) long?

2 What comes next: Mexico, Belize, Guatemala, El Salvador, Honduras, Nicaragua, Costa Rica, ...?

3 Which lake on the Peru-Bolivia border is S. America's largest and the world's highest body of navigable water?

4 On which Caribbean island would you find the town of Montego Bay?

5 In which country is the Atacama Desert, one of the driest areas of the world?

6 Only two of the 13 countries in South America do not have a coastline. Name one of them.

7 Two countries comprise the Caribbean island of Hispaniola – the Dominican Republic and ....?

8 The Angel Falls, the world's highest, are in the interior of which South American country?

9 What is the name of the Mexican peninsula that forms the southern lip of the Gulf of Mexico?

10 Which island in the Caribbean (or "the West Indies"), formerly British, is the furthest east?

11 What is the biggest city in South America, in terms of population?

12 What is the capital of Cuba, famous for its lively night life until the revolution?

13 The Galapagos Islands, famous for their unusual flora and fauna, form a province of which country?

14 The United States sent its troops "to restore order" on which Caribbean island in 1983?

15 Which pre-Spanish Mexican civilisation came next: Olmec, Zapotec, Toltec, Maya, ...?

16 The Caribbean islands of Guadeloupe and Martinique are "departments" of which country?

17 Brazil is the largest country in South America. What is the second largest?

18 Name two of the four countries in South America who do *not* have Spanish as an official language.

19 Which Caribbean island's volcanic mountains are represented on its flag in black and yellow triangles?

20 Macchu Picchu, the town built high in the Andes by the Incas against the Spanish, is in which country?

21 What do the Argentinians, who claim ownership of the islands, call the Falklands?

22 What is the jet-set resort on the Pacific coast of Mexico, famous for its cliff divers?

23 Medellín is notorious as the "cocaine capital" of which South American country?

24 The Virgin Islands in the Caribbean are divided between which two nations?

25 What is the Spanish name of the island at the foot of South America, meaning "land of fire"?

26 Devil's Island, the infamous penal colony featured in the film *Papillon*, was in which S. American country?

27 What creature does the eagle in the Mexican flag hold in its beak?

28 The capitals of Argentina and Uruguay, Buenos Aires and Montevideo, share which river estuary?

29 Which orange-favoured liqueur takes its name from a Dutch-owned island off the coast of Venezuela?

30 When was the Panama Canal opened to shipping: 1874, 1894, 1914 or 1934?

WHAT HE NEEDS IS A GOOD KICKING.

Answers on page 213

Knowall's question:

Which African mountain has snow on its peak all year round?

THERE ISN'T ONE !!!

1 What is the most populous country in Africa?

2 How many countries border Zaïre: 3, 5, 7, 9 or 11?

3 In which country is the old walled city of Timbuktu?

4 The Hutu and Tutsi live in which two nations?

5 Who met whom at Ujiji in 1871?

6 The Canary Isles are off the coast of which country?

7 Mogadishu is the capital of which East African country?

8 "... great, grey-green, greasy ...." (Kipling). Which river?

9 What is the most populous city in Africa?

10 Odd one out: Libya, Togo, Gabon, Angola, Zambia?

11 Which country's flag features a Masai warrior's shield?

12 The Victoria Falls are on which southern African river?

13 Which country was called the Gold Coast until 1957?

14 How did Liberia get its name?

15 Tanganyika and Zanzibar became what in 1964?

16 Which mountains run through Morocco and Algeria?

17 Eritrea pronounced independence in 1993. From whom?

18 Cape Town lies below which famous natural feature?

19 The most northerly point of Africa is in which country?

20 The White and Blue Nile meet at which Sudanese city?

21 Côte d'Ivoire is the official name of which country?

22 What is Africa's second longest river?

23 Which is the biggest country in Africa?

24 What links Guinea, Mali, Niger, Benin and Nigeria?

25 How many African nations have Guinea in their name?

26 The Suez Canal runs through which African country?

27 What is the unit of currency in South Africa?

28 Malawi, Mali, Mauritania, Morocco, M........?

29 Uganda, Kenya and Tanzania all border which lake?

30 South-West Africa became what nation in 1990?

I'LL KILL MYSELF LAUGHING IF THIS CARRIES ON.

Answers on page 213

Knowall's question:

What is the national anthem of Australia?

WALTZING MATILDA !!!

1 What island was known as Van Dieman's Land until 1855?

2 Which Pacific atoll, used for nuclear tests by the USA, gave its name to an article of swimwear?

3 What's missing: Queensland, Victoria, Tasmania, S. Australia, W. Australia, Northern Territory?

4 What is the name of the stretch of sea separating the North and South islands of New Zealand?

5 What famous monolith, the world's largest, is a sacred Aborigine site in the centre of Australia?

6 What is the capital of Papua New Guinea, the country that forms the eastern part of the island?

7 The Olympic Games of 1956 were held in which Australian city?

8 Which Pacific island, measuring 21sq km (8 square miles) is the world's smallest republic?

9 What is the name of the species of Australian marsupial, similar to the kangaroo but smaller?

10 What film of 1993 was set in 19th-century New Zealand and concerned a musical instrument?

11 What natural feature lies off the Queensland coast and extends over 250,000sq km (100,000 square miles).

12 Which Pacific country withdrew from the British Commonwealth of Nations in 1987?

13 The capital of Australia is located inside a region called the Australian Capital Territory. What is it?

14 What is the name given to the native population of New Zealand?

15 Meaning "hole in the ground", Coober Pedy in S. Australia is known for the mining of which stone?

16 Which group of islands in the Pacific are divided into two countries, "Western" and "American"?

17 What northern Australian town was bombed by the Japanese air force during World War 2?

18 The capital of New Zealand is the world's most southerly capital city. What is it?

19 Mt Kosciusko, Australia's highest peak, is in which range of mountains?

20 Which fish provides the biggest source of income for the economy of the Solomon Islands?

21 Fremantle is the ocean port of which Australian state's capital city?

22 What do New Caledonia, French Polynesia and the Wallis & Futuna Islands have in common?

23 In which Australian city would you find the world-famous Bondi Beach?

24 Formerly the Friendly Islands, which South Pacific nation is governed by King Taufa'ahau Tupou IV?

25 What mineral was discovered at Kalgoorlie, Western Australia, in 1887?

26 Which island group in the Pacific Ocean finally gained independence from the USA in 1996?

27 The Canterbury Plains of New Zealand's South Island are famous for producing what animal?

28 What is the name of the airborne medical service provided for isolated Australian homesteads?

29 Name the Pacific island inhabited by descendants of nine mutineers from HMS *Bounty* since1790.

30 Which salt "lake" – Australia's largest and its lowest point – is used for land speed record attempts?

HIT THE FAST-FORWARD BUTTON ON THIS ONE.

Answers on page 213

QUIZ NUMBER 37

Knowall's question:

What is the capital of Pakistan?

KARACHI !!!

1 What is the name of the historic pass into the north-west frontier of Pakistan from Afghanistan?

2 Seoul hosted the summer Olympic Games in 1988. Which Asian city was the first to hold them, in 1964?

3 The lowest point on the Earth's surface lies in Asia. What is it?

4 After Russia, China is the biggest country of Asia. Which one comes third?

5 By what name was Thailand ("land of the free") known in the West before 1939?

6 Which railway, the world's longest, links Moscow with Vladivostok, on the Pacific coast of Russia?

7 What is strange about the title of the movie *Krakatoa, East of Java*?

8 The city of Benares (Varanasi), a destination for millions of Hindu pilgrims, is on which "holy" river?

9 Mt Everest is the world's highest mountain. What peak, located in the Karakorams, comes second?

10 What is the largest city of the People's Republic of China, in terms of population?

11 Siberia's Lake Baikal contains how much of the world's "fresh" lake water: 1%, 5%, 10%, 15% or 20%?

12 The Seikan, the world's longest undersea rail tunnel, connects which two Japanese islands?

13 Asia contains the only country in the world beginning with a Q. What is it?

14 The name of Saigon was changed in 1976 on the reunification of Vietnam. What is it now called?

15 What is the tiny country squashed between India and China whose name means "land of the dragon"?

16 Which city in Malaysia completed the world's highest habitable building in 1996?

17 Which Asian country is unique in the world in having a flag which is not rectangular?

18 Soil (loess) washed into it gives the huge Hwang-Ho River in China its more common name. What is it?

19 The world's most sparsely populated country lies in Asia. What is it?

20 Middle East news has frequent references to "the West Bank". The west bank of what?

21 India and Pakistan have neighbouring states of the same name, meaning "land of five rivers". What is it?

22 What Asian country was called Ceylon until the new Socialist government changed its name in 1972?

23 Which is the odd one out: Damascus, Baghdad, Tehran, Kabul, Calcutta, Bangkok, Djakarta?

24 Muslims are expected to attempt a pilgrimage at some stage of their lives to which holy city in Saudi Arabia?

25 Which modernised island nation state lies at the southern tip of the Malay Peninsula?

26 The Shatt-al-Arab Waterway was the scene of battles between which two nations from 1980 to 1988?

27 Japan's second largest city grew as the main port for Tokyo, the biggest. What is it?

28 Which Asian country has the world's largest film industry and greatest number of cinemas?

29 What is the English name of the "autonomous region" of south-west China that the Chinese call Xizang?

30 Why are the group of islands between China and Indonesia called the Philippines?

NOT A BAD ANSWER, BUT WRONG.

Answers on page 213

Knowall's question:

Which European country is the world's biggest producer of false teeth?

IT MUST BE HUNGARY !!!

1 Name one of the three cities which lay claim to the title "Venice of the North".

2 The state of Yugoslavia now comprises Serbia and which other republic?

3 Which range of mountains separates European Russia from Asian Russia (Siberia)?

4 Which small country became Europe's newest independent nation state in the 1990s?

5 After Berlin and Hamburg, what is the third largest German-speaking city?

6 What is the name given to the part of Denmark that is a peninsula?

7 Majorca, Minorca and Ibiza belong to which group of Mediterranean islands?

8 Name one of the two independent states that are totally surrounded by Italy.

9 Which Greek mountain has been forbidden to women since the 11th century?

10 What river links Ulm, Linz, Vienna, Bratislava, Budapest and Belgrade?

11 What is Europe's highest capital city, at a height of 655m (2,183ft).

12 In which European country will you get 100 grozny for one zloty?

13 The river on which Rome stands gave its name to a famous Roman emperor. What is it?

14 What is the most southerly county in the Republic of Ireland?

15 Transylvania forms the north-west region of which Eastern European country?

16 Before German reunification in 1990 the city of Chemnitz had a distinctly Communist name. What?

17 What is the largest island of Europe, over twice as big as its nearest challenger?

18 What's next: Denmark, Poland, Czech Republic, Austria, Switzerland, France, Luxembourg, Belgium?

19 In which Swiss city are the headquarters of the International Red Cross?

20 What and where is Maelstrom, a word we use to describe a whirlpool or great state of confusion?

21 After European Russia, what is the largest country in Europe? *(Only true since 1991.)*

22 What is the name of the range of mountains that forms "the backbone of Italy".

23 What is the name of the cold northerly summer wind that blows down the Rhône Valley of southern France?

24 Which city in Catalonia is Spain's largest industrial centre and its biggest port?

25 What was St Petersburg, Russia's second largest city, called between 1924 and 1991?

26 Mt Blanc is on the border on which two European countries?

27 What is the political capital of the Netherlands and home to the International Court of Justice?

28 Name the marshy area of the Rhône delta in southern France renowned for its white horses.

29 Which Scandinavian country is known to its own people as Suomi?

30 In which Italian city would you find La Scala opera house and the San Siro football stadium?

THAT ANSWER TAKES SOME LICKING.

Answers on page 214

Knowall's question:

What did Kevin Leech buy for £6 million in May 1996?

ALAN SHEARER !!!

1. Which English city has a bigger canal system than Venice?

2. Of the 10 highest mountains in the UK, how many are located in Scotland?

3. The columns of the Giant's Causeway, in Antrim, Northern Ireland, consist of what rock?

4. What is the island off the north-west coast of Wales, separated from the mainland by the Menai Strait?

5. In which town in Kent is the Red Indian princess Pocahontas buried?

6. The ferry from Stranraer, in south-west Scotland, takes you to which port in Northern Ireland?

7. The River Thames rises in Gloucestershire among which English hills?

8. The world's longest suspension bridge spans a river estuary in England. What is it?

9. What "great glen" links Fort William in the south-west with Inverness in the north-east?

10. What is the largest lake in the Lake District, and the largest in England?

11. Britain's biggest container port is in Suffolk, on the coast of East Anglia. Where?

12. What is the name of the Marquis of Bath's stately home, located in Wiltshire?

13. Where in Britain are Herm, Jethou, Brechou, Lihou and the Minquiers?

14. What is the name of the last surviving coalmine in South Wales, now profitable after a buyout?

15. Spot the odd one out: Truro, Taunton, Winchester, Derby, Chester, Lincoln, Maidstone.

16 Which city has the tallest spire in England at 123 metres (404 feet)?

17 What links Welshpool, Shrewsbury, Ironbridge, Worcester and Gloucester?

18 Name the area of shallow sea between the coasts of Lincolnshire and Norfolk.

19 What was the royal residence on the Isle of Wight that was Queen Victoria's favourite home?

20 In which century was the first recorded sighting of a monster in Loch Ness: 6th, 12th, 17th, or 20th?

21 What is the highest mountain in England, rising to a modest 978m (3,210ft)?

22 The county town of Buckinghamshire is not *Buckingham*. What is it?

23 Located in Northern Ireland, it is the largest lake in the United Kingdom. Can you name it?

24 What's next: Cornwall, Devon, Dorset, Hampshire, West Sussex, East Sussex, ...?

25 Which Hebrides island was connected to the mainland by a bridge completed in 1995?

26 Every year Appleby, in Cumbria, is the scene of a specialist fair. What is its theme?

27 Built by the Romans, Hadrian's Wall runs from the Solway Firth in the west to where in the east?

28 Stoke-on-Trent is the centre of an industrial area known traditionally as what?

29 Which former major fishing port is the most easterly town in the British Isles?

30 What is the capital town of the Isle of Man, located on the east coast of the island?

HE'S BURNING THE CANDLE AT BOTH ENDS.

Answers on page 214

Knowall's question:

What used to stand at Tyburn,
at the end of Oxford Street?

MARBLE ARCH !!!

1 What used to be traded at Covent Garden Market, now a popular tourist centre?

2 From 1863, what linked Paddington in the west with Moorgate in the east?

3 In which London street can the Royal Courts of Justice be found?

4 What new airport within the capital, specialising in business flights to Europe, opened in 1987?

5 In which development close to Tower Bridge is the World Trade Centre located?

6 What tall monument completed in 1842 was built with granite from as far afield as Cornwall and Scotland?

7 What West End street, site of the first-ever boutique, became synonymous with London's "Swinging Sixties"?

8 In what part of London was the first factory where Royal Doulton pottery was manufactured?

9 Which park north of Marylebone is the location for London's Zoological Gardens?

10 What area giving its name to a group of writers and painters in the 1920s is home to the British Museum?

11 Which London hospital founded in 1122 stands beside Smithfield Market?

12 Who used to live at the simple but famous address "Number One, London"?

13 A working reconstruction of which Shakespearean theatre was opened in 1996?

14 Name the official London residence of the chancellor of the exchequer.

15 Which iron pedestrian bridge across the River Thames connects Charing Cross and Waterloo?

16 Which area, almost surrounded by the River Thames, is the heart of London's Docklands development?

17 What riding resort in Hyde Park was named after a corruption of the French *route de roi* (king's drive)?

18 Which great church was completed on a site near Victoria Station in 1903?

19 From what material is the winged statue of Eros in Piccadilly Circus made?

20 Victoria & Albert, Science and Natural History Museums were built on land bought with the profits of what?

21 Mentioned in Dickens' *Little Dorrit,* what is the only surviving galleried inn in London?

22 Name the Hackney park which was the first large purpose-designed public open space in London.

23 What then recently completed venue was the home of the 1924-25 British Empire Exhibition?

24 Supported by George IV, which architect undertook an ambitious redevelopment of Regent Street?

25 Which three bastions of the English legal profession are found off Victoria Embankment?

26 Name three of the five city gates of the Roman fort city of Londinium.

27 Which great fish market, now relocated to East London, once operated beside the Tower of London?

28 What did Americans buy for reassembly in Arizona, allegedly thinking they were getting Tower Bridge?

29 Which cricket ground is the home of the Marylebone Cricket Club?

30 Which royal palaces beside the Thames burned down in 1698 and 1834 respectively?

HE SHOULD BE HUNG FOR ANSWERS LIKE THAT.

Answers on page 214

Knowall's question:

Complete the sequence:
George I, George II,
George III, George IV ?

GEORGE V !!!

1 Truman, Eisenhower, Kennedy, Johnson, Nixon ?

2 Alpha, beta, gamma, delta ?

3 Everton, Manchester United, Liverpool, Coventry ?

4 Mercury, Venus, Earth, Mars, Jupiter ?

5 Millimetre, centimetre, decimetre, metre ?

6 2, 5, 9, 14, 20, 27 ?

7 Golf, Hotel, India, Juliet, Kilo, Lima, Mike ?

8 Montreal, Moscow, Los Angeles, Seoul, Barcelona ?

9 Triangle, square, pentagon, hexagon, heptagon ?

10 Dogger, Fisher, German Bight, Humber, Thames ?

11 Chinese, English, Spanish, Hindi, Arabic, Bengali ?

12 Hydrogen, helium, lithium, beryllium, boron ?

13 Aries, Taurus, Gemini, Cancer, Leo, Virgo, Libra ?

14 Attlee, Churchill, Eden, Macmillan, Douglas-Home ?

15 Gale, strong gale, storm, violent storm ?

16 Pius XII, John XIII, Paul VI, John Paul I ?

17 Q, W, E, R, T, Y, U, I, O ?

18 Kokaku, Ninko, Komei, Meiji, Taisho, Hirohito ?

19 Breve, semibreve, minim, crotchet, quaver ?

20 Connery, Lazenby, Moore, Dalton ?

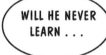

21 *Love Me Do, Please Please Me, From Me To You* ?

22 Khrushchev, Brezhnev, Andropov, Chernenko ?

23 W. Germany, Argentina, Italy, Argentina, W. Germany ?

24 Field marshal, general(s), colonel(s), major ?

25 China, India, USA, Indonesia, Brazil, Russia, Pakistan ?

26 Vauxhall, Lambeth, Westminster, Waterloo, Blackfriars ?

27 De Gaulle, Pompidou, Giscard d'Estaing, Mitterand ?

28 Bridges, Masefield, Day Lewis, Betjeman ?

29 Alabama, Alaska, Arizona, Arkansas, California ?

30 Red, orange, yellow, green, blue, indigo ?

Answers on page 215

Knowall's question:

By what name is the Orion nebula more commonly known?

THE PLOUGH !!!

1 What is the popular name for the massive explosion believed by many to have created the Universe?

2 Who revolutionised scientific thought by proving that the Earth rotated around the Sun?

3 In space exploration terms, what does the acronym NASA stand for?

4 What was the first man-made object that went into Earth orbit?

5 Which Italian was the first scientist to use a telescope to study the stars?

6 What key astronomical feature did early sailors use to help them navigate in the Northern Hemisphere?

7 Which American space probe sent back the first close-up pictures of Mars to Earth?

8 What is the astronomical significance of the star *Proxima Centauri*?

9 By what name is the spectacular phenomenon *Aurora Borealis* better known?

10 What scientific name do astronomers give to an exploding star?

11 Which planet, sometimes observed shining brightly, is known as "The Evening Star"?

12 In astronomical terms, what is the definition of the phenomenon known as a "black hole"?

13 Name the Russian space station which featured in a joint mission with the USA in 1995.

14 Only 16 months after it was first discovered, the Shoemaker-Levy Comet smashed into which planet?

15 Name the first astronaut to breach the "final frontier" and represent Britain in space.

16 What planet in the solar system is named after the Roman god of the sea?

17 The constellation *Ursa Major* has various nicknames, but what is the literal translation of the title?

18 Why is the place of Laika assured in the annals of space travel?

19 What is the name of the galaxy in which our own solar system is located?

20 Which ill-fated lunar mission was the subject of an award-winning film in the 1990s?

21 For what achievement will Russian cosmonaut Alexii Leonov always be remembered?

22 Which US space shuttle mission came to a disastrous end in 1986?

23 Who was the first man in space, and in what year did this achievement take place?

24 Which Greek astronomer propounded the geocentric theory of the Universe in the second century AD?

25 Which planet in our own solar system orbits closest to the Sun?

26 What was the name of the first US space shuttle, and in what year did it first fly?

27 Neil Armstrong was the first man to walk on the Moon. Who was the second?

28 To the nearest day, how many days does the Moon take to orbit the Earth?

29 Which physicist provided an accessible theory of the Universe in his book *A Brief History of Time*?

30 In which year was Halley's Comet last visible from Earth: 1970, 1974, 1978, 1982 or 1986?

Answers on page 215

Knowall's question:

What did Thomas Swan invent in 1878?

THE CYGNET RING !!!

1 What is so significant about the American submarine USS *Nautilus*?

2 From which location did the BBC make its very first televised broadcast in 1936?

3 What incident is said to have inspired Isaac Newton's theory of gravity?

4 State Albert Einstein's ground-breaking formula for the theory of relativity.

5 Antoine Lavoisier was one of the fathers of modern chemistry. How did he die?

6 What colour does litmus paper turn when dipped in an acidic liquid?

7 For what mechanical device was William Burroughs granted a US patent in 1891?

8 Which Scotsman was instrumental in the invention of the telephone?

9 What bat-like technology is used to detect submerged submarines?

10 Which useful culinary device was invented by French physicist Denis Papin in 1680?

11 In 1851 Americans Elias Howe, Walter Hunt and Isaac Singer independently invented what?

12 What accelerates a chemical reaction without itself being changed?

13 In what process, named after its inventor, is heat used to kill bacteria?

14 Divers use "Scuba" equipment. What does that acronym stand for?

15 Which statesman used a kite fitted with a key to demonstrate that lightning is a form of electricity?

16 What did medieval alchemists believe would change base metals into pure gold?

17 Road builder Blind Jack of Knaresborough built over 174 miles (280km) of what in the Middle Ages?

18 Which element did English nobleman Henry Cavendish discover in 1776?

19 In 1884, who developed the first ink-storing pen fit for mass production?

20 What major British scientific institution was founded in 1662 during the reign of Charles II?

21 By what name is the "artifical silk" perfected by Wallace Carothers in 1937 known?

22 With whom is the development of the first pneumatic tyre associated?

23 In 1867, C. L. Sholes invented the first typewriter. With what gunmaking firm did he sign a production deal?

24 The name of which chemical element contains just three letters?

25 What did Wilhelm von Roentgen discover by mistake in 1895 which later had a valuable medical application?

26 Which Ancient Greek exclaimed "Eureka!" ("I've found it!") whilst in his bath?

27 What significant product invented by Thomas Edison in 1877 was first marketed as a toy?

28 Finished in 1945, weighed 30 tons, occupied 1,500 square feet, had 18,000 thermionic valves. What was it?

29 Which Greek thinker and scholar wrote the influential mathematical work *Elements*?

30 In 1802, what over-ambitious idea did Albert Mathieu suggest to Napoleon for invading England?

HE'S A REALLY BRIGHT SPARK.

Answers on page 215

Knowall's question:

Which French brothers are known as "The fathers of cinema"?

THE WARNER BROTHERS !!!

1 What new camera did Edwin Land invent in 1937?

2 Electroencephalography is the study of what?

3 What is the most abundant metal on Earth?

4 Who was "The Wizard of Melno Park"?

5 What are woofers and tweeters?

6 Name the three ways in which heat can travel.

7 How long is a Myr in geological time?

8 Who is identified with the theory of natural selection?

9 What did undertaker A. B. Strowger invent in 1891?

10 Who made the Wild West's "Peacemaker" revolver?

11 To what relationship does Boyle's Law apply?

12 What gas is used to lift modern airships?

13 Alessandro Volta's major electrical "first" was what?

14 In which three states can matter exist?

15 Which metal derives its name from the Devil?

16 What unit is used to measure resistance?

17 Steve Jobs and Steve Wozniak founded which company?

18 What does the acronym Radar stand for?

19 At what Centigrade temperature is Absolute Zero?

20 Who was the first person to win two Nobel prizes?

21 Which substance has the chemical formula H_2SO_4?

22 For what would a bowdrill be used?

23 Who first developed wireless transmission?

24 Letterpress is a technique for doing what?

25 What is the everyday name of sodium chloride?

26 Who invented the modern safety lift?

27 What was Archimedes' Screw?

28 Brass is an alloy of which two metals?

29 Which Swedish manufacturer invented dynamite?

30 What does the science of ethology study?

Answers on page 215

QUIZ NUMBER 45

Knowall's question:

What form of communication began in 1844 with the message "What hath God wrought?"?

THE PONY EXPRESS !!!

1 What innovative amphibious vehicle did Briton Christopher Cockerell invent in the 1950s?

2 In photographic terms, what do the letters SLR in front of the word camera stand for?

3 What fibre optic device is used by doctors to conduct non-surgical internal examinations of patients?

4 Which British aeronautical engineer developed the first jet engine to power an aircraft?

5 In 1643, Galileo's pupil Evangelista Toricelli invented what instrument for measuring air pressure?

6 Who developed Germany's wartime V2 and became a mainstay of America's rocket programme?

7 Hiram Maxim and Richard Gatling each developed early forms of what?

8 Which 17th-century instrument maker, inventor and steam pioneer first used the unit of "horsepower"?

9 In 1937, Chester Carlson invented "xerography". What office machine was developed from this discovery?

10 What did Dutchman Cornelius Drebbel test on the River Thames in 1620?

11 Which French physicist invented the gyroscope and used a pendulum to show that the Earth rotates?

12 "The most significant invention of the 20th century" was made by Jack Kilby in 1958. What was it?

13 The "Manhattan Project" was the codename for the development of what weapon in the United States?

14 What instrument did early sailors use to determine longitude and the time of day?

15 In 1924, what did the Computing-Tabulating-Recording Company become?

16 In the early 1700s, what did Thomas Newcomen and Thomas Savery develop for the mining industry?

17 What is created when light from a laser interfaces with light from a photographic plate or film?

18 What is Thomas Crapper generally credited with perfecting in the 19th century?

19 Name the world's first commercially produced vertical-take-off "jump jet".

20 Hans Oersted changed the course of history in 1820 by discovering the link between which two forces?

21 What machine was largely unchanged until the 19th century following its invention by Gutenberg in 1450?

22 In 1709, which British ironmaster developed the "blast" furnace, burning coke and lime to smelt iron ore?

23 British scientist James Dewar developed what in 1892 to facilitate the cold storage of liquid oxygen?

24 What instrument was invented by Galileo and refined by German scientist Gabriel Fahrenheit in 1714?

25 Which French oceanographer is credited with the invention of the aqualung?

26 In 1943 the world's first electronic computer, Colossus, was built in Britain. What was its specific purpose?

27 What sacred Catholic relic was finally declared a medieval fake after scientific tests in 1988?

28 Who developed and marketed the first effective electronic pocket calculator in Britain?

29 Supply the missing word in this firearms sequence: matchlock, wheel-lock, ..., percussion lock.

30 What "first" was achieved in 1835 when a horse-drawn reaper was joined to a threshing machine?

HE DRIVES ME UP THE POLE.

Answers on page 216

Knowall's question:

For what specific purpose did the London County Council set up a fleet of motorised ambulances in 1905?

TO COLLECT PATIENTS !!!

1 Before the advent of the internal combustion engine, for what was petroleum principally used?

2 What Russian supersonic airliner based on stolen Concorde plans crashed at the 1973 Paris Air Show?

3 Professor Charles Page built America's first electric locomotive in which year: 1819, 1839, 1859, 1879?

4 Name the German family of five brothers who turned from making sewing machines to cars around 1900.

5 Which Cornishman built Britain's first "self-propelled road conveyance" in 1801?

6 In the 1930s, the world speed record for steam power was set at 126mph by what streamlined locomotive?

7 In 1925, America's General Motors failed in a bid for which British car company?

8 Where did the world's first motor-racing Grand Prix take place in 1906?

9 Name the Sail Training Association's "tall ship" built in 1965 to give youngsters sailing experience.

10 Which Polish-born engineer was largely responsible for the helicopter's development in America?

11 Name the Brunel steamship launched in 1843, recovered from the Falkland Islands to be restored at Bristol.

12 Which maker of luxury grand touring cars based at Newport Pagnell is now owned by Ford?

13 What was the significance of the *Stourbridge Lion*, imported to America from Britain in 1829?

14 To what did William Lyons' SS Car Company change its name in 1945?

15 In what year was the North American transcontinental railway completed: 1849, 1859, 1869, 1879, 1889?

16 When Henry Ford formed the Ford Motor Company, what did the old Henry Ford Company become?

17 In 1919, a Farman Goliath aircraft carried passengers between which two European cities for the first time?

18 What famous British car company had a works at Springfield, Massachusetts from 1927 to 1931?

19 The world's first electric railway began operation on the seafront of which British resort in 1879?

20 MG is the most famous marque in British sports car history. What did the letters stand for?

21 Which firm from Thetford, Norfolk was pre-eminent in the manufacture of 19th-century traction engines?

22 Who bought Britain's Rover car company from British Aerospace in 1994?

23 In 1968, Lockheed introduced the world's largest aircraft, a military transport plane. What is it called?

24 What is the name of France's high-speed 1980s passenger trains which run on special tracks?

25 Which red high-performance cars bear the famous "Prancing Horse" badge?

26 How many Model 'T' Fords were made before the production run ended in 1926: 5, 10, 15 or 20 million?

27 Who was killed trying to set a new water speed record on Lake Windermere in June 1930?

28 What company operates passenger train services throughout the USA?

29 Which three countries signed a 1967 deal to develop and market European Airbus airliners?

30 What news led 340,000 emigrants to take ship from Liverpool to Australia in the 1850s?

HE ACCIDENTALLY OVERLOOKED THE WORD "SPECIFIC".

Answers on page 216

Knowall's question:

What liner won The Blue Riband for the fastest Atlantic crossing in 1907, on only her second westbound voyage?

THE *TITANIC* !!!

1 What notable transport "first" linked Stockton and Darlington in 1825?

2 In 1888, who advertised his "Patent Motor Car" in the German technical press?

3 What baby car appeared in Britain in 1922 to press comments like "get one for each foot"?

4 In what year did the London Underground run its first electric tube train: 1895, 1904, 1913, 1917, 1922?

5 Frenchman Ferdinand de Lesseps was responsible for the construction of what major waterway?

6 Which American car company took over the British Rootes Group in 1967?

7 In 1908, what unfortunate aviation "first" was recorded by Lieutenant Thomas Selfridge at Fort Myer, Virginia?

8 What does the acronym RoRo stand for in passenger shipping terms?

9 In what year were steam locomotives finally phased out of the British railway system?

10 Which car company was formed by pioneering manufacturer Ransom Eli Olds in 1896?

11 How many transport horses were there in Britain in 1800: 1 million, 2 million, 3 million, 4 million?

12 Which car did Steve McQueen drive to spectacular effect in the film *Bullitt*?

13 What future opportunity to "visit" space was offered to *all* Americans who could afford it in the 1990s?

14 The fears of defence chiefs caused the cancellation of what major Anglo-French transport project in 1907?

15 Which American port city was the birthplace of fast sailing clippers in the 19th century?

16 How many car manufacturing companies were there in America before World War 1: 550, 1,300, 2,100, 2,900?

17 In 1962, what form of public transport was withdrawn from the streets of London?

18 What is the seaman's name for the area of ceaseless wind and storm in high southern latitudes?

19 What motoring curiosities were offered by Isetta and Messerschmitt in the late 1950s?

20 Italian Prince Borghese won an 8,000-mile automobile race from Paris to which oriental city in 1907?

21 Which locomotive reached a record speed of 97.5mph (157km/h) on the London to Leeds run in 1934?

22 What container port on the Thames replaced the Port of London Docks as they closed down?

23 Which maker received the first royal warrant as a supplier of motor cars to the Crown?

24 What propelled Léon Serpollet's car when he broke the world speed record at 110 km/h (74 mph) in 1902?

25 The name of which 19th-century American maker has become synonymous with luxury railway cars?

26 What prestigious cruise liner was requisitioned as a hospital ship during the Falklands War?

27 Which 1980s gull-wing sportscar was produced in Northern Ireland before the company went bust?

28 In 1992 the plans for what new facility at Heathrow Airport were announced?

29 What ill-fated high-speed train with a revolutionary tilting mechanism was revealed by British Rail in 1981?

30 Until Henry Ford formed his own company in 1903, which great inventor-friend employed him?

WRONG, BUT I STILL GET THAT SINKING FEELING.

Answers on page 216

QUIZ NUMBER 48

Knowall's question:

The racing cars of which Italian manufacturer scored over 2,000 victories in the 1920s?

FERRARI !!!

1 Between which two English cities did the Great Western Railway originally run?

2 A 14,000-mile race ended in London with *Taeping* and *Ariel* 20 minutes apart. What type of ships were they?

3 The motor age began in 1886 with a present of a "horseless carriage" to whose wife?

4 In 1925, what type of aircraft with a free-spinning rotor blade on top was tested at Farnborough?

5 Which famous car marque appeared in 1901, named after the daughter of French importer Emil Jellinek?

6 In November 1991 what memorable excuse did British Rail offer for the delay of many trains?

7 Between 1760 and 1790 almost 4,000 miles of what was built in Britain at a cost of some £11 million?

8 From 1925, what did Grand Prix racing drivers no longer have to carry in their cars?

9 What aviation "first" was achieved by an aircraft that travelled from Hendon to Windsor in 1911?

10 Which former Cunard liner was a floating university in Hong Kong before it burned and sank in 1972?

11 In May 1959, who claimed a new world water speed record for Britain at 260 mph (418 km/h)?

12 In the early 1990s Virgin boss Richard Branson was involved in a "dirty tricks" row with what airline?

13 With which Japanese car manufacturer did British Leyland form a working partnership in 1981?

14 What locomotive was made by Hackworth for the Liverpool & Manchester Railway's 1830 Rainhill Trials?

15 Britain produced the world's first jet airliner, which was dogged by a series of mystery crashes. Name it.

16 Which Scot started the American car company which became the foundation of General Motors?

17 In 1909, who won the *Daily Mail*'s £1,000 prize for the first aircraft crossing of the English Channel?

18 What powered the torpedo-like French car that set a world land speed record of 105 km/h (70 mph) in 1899?

19 What is the popular name given to early pedal-cycles officially described as "ordinaries"?

20 Name the British car marque that produced Mulliner-bodied "Continental" models after World War 2.

21 What did a B-25 bomber crash into in New York on 28 July 1945 with the loss of 13 lives?

22 In 1953 Ford of Britain launched the world's then-cheapest car at £390 including tax. What was it?

23 What was completed in 1913 when President Wilson set off a dynamite blast 4,000 miles away from his desk?

24 Which new London Underground line was opened by the Queen in March 1969?

25 What car maker in the former Eastern Bloc has been taken over by Volkswagen?

26 How many passengers will the "Super Jumbo" Boeing 747-600 announced in 1996 carry: 495, 545, 595, 645?

27 Which Worcestershire-based British manufacturer still produces sports cars using traditional methods?

28 The first novelty bicycles were propelled with the feet rather than pedals. What were they called?

29 In 1913, what was the first car ever offered for sale by William Morris (later Lord Nuffield)?

30 The sturdy sailing ship *Charles W. Morgan* is preserved in New England. For what purpose was she built?

SOMETIMES HE REALLY BUGS ME.

Answers on page 217

QUIZ NUMBER 49

Knowall's question:

Which Australian animal's Aborigine name means "no drink"?

EMU !!!

1 Of all the mammals, which species lives the longest?

2 What is the largest land animal?

3 Name one of the two mammals that lays eggs.

4 How many stomachs does a cow have?

5 What animal's name means "river horse" in Greek?

6 Mozzarella cheese comes from which animal?

7 How many teeth do anteaters have?

8 *Gorilla gorilla* is the Latin name for which animal?

9 Wallabies belong to which class of mammal?

10 The word "ursine" describes which kind of animal?

11 What creature's name means "wild man of the woods"?

12 Which animal is named after one of the "deadly sins"?

13 What are the houses that beavers build called?

14 What is the world's biggest spider?

15 What is the largest member of the whale family?

16 Which type of camel has two humps?

17 The okapi is the nearest living relative of which animal?

18 What are rhino horns made of?

19 The millipede's record leg count is: 750, 1,000 or 1,400?

20 What is the fastest mammal?

21 The ibex is a kind of antelope, deer, goat or sheep?

22 What is the main diet of the giant panda?

23 Which is the only mammal that can truly be said to fly?

24 What is the name given to a female donkey?

25 Found in the south-west USA, a sidewinder is what?

26 What was the name of London Zoo's famous elephant?

27 If a dog barks and a cow moos, what animal "gibbers"?

28 What is the more common name for the gnu?

29 How many teeth do dogs have: 18, 24, 30, 36, 42?

30 What is the branch of biology which studies animals?

HE'S BARKING UP A GUM TREE.

Answers on page 217

Knowall's question:

From which country did the turkey originate?

TURKEY !!!

1 Which animal is considered sacred by the Hindus?

2 Tigers are found in India, Africa or South America?

3 Adder's poison acts on which part of the body?

4 Animals that sleep through winter are said to do what?

5 Geckos are small types of which sort of animal?

6 What is the world's largest species of snake?

7 How many legs do spiders have: 4, 6, 8 or 10?

8 The kodiak is the tallest breed of which animal?

9 A camel's hump contains fat, muscle or water?

10 Mules are a cross between which two animals?

11 Lupine describes the attributes of what kind of animal?

12 Which three animals starred in *The Incredible Journey*?

13 What is the world's largest lizard?

14 Name the only monkey that is native to Europe.

15 Animals that live in water and on land are called what?

16 Name the otter that Henry Williamson wrote about.

17 What animal provides the hide for "shammy" leather?

18 Which species is not a bat: mastiff, hoary or ridgeback?

19 Horseshoe crabs belong to which class of animal?

20 What is a baby kangaroo called?

21 Guanacos and vicunas are cousins of which mammal?

22 What distinguishing feature did Clarence the lion have?

23 How high can fleas jump: 30, 45, or 60cm (12, 18, 24in)?

24 What animal did the Romans call the horse-tiger?

25 What endangered animal can be black, white or Indian?

26 Which male animals are sometimes seen "in velvet"?

27 In the Kipling stories, what animal was Rikki-tikki-tavi?

28 What is the national animal of South Africa?

29 Which insect carries the tropical disease of malaria?

30 Why do snakes flick out their tongues?

Answers on page 217

Knowall's question:

What is Britain's biggest spider: cardinal, garden, harvestman, house or wolf?

WOLF !!!

1 Which amphibious mammal lives in a holt?

2 What are the most common types of creature in the UK?

3 From what animals has the ferret descended?

4 A muntjac is what kind of animal?

5 In the *Wind in the Willows,* who suffered from road rage?

6 Which is Britain's largest deer: fallow, musk, red or roe?

7 What is the only poisonous snake found in Britain?

8 Myxomatosis has killed millions of which animal?

9 Which insect has the Latin name *Apis mellifera*?

10 What is the name of a badger's home?

11 What is Britain's smallest mammal?

12 Which animal brought the bubonic plague to London?

13 Which rodent fell asleep at the Mad Hatter's tea party?

14 The hair of which animal was used for shaving brushes?

15 What speedy animal rests in a form?

16 Which two animals farmed for fur breed in the wild?

17 What is a stoat called when it turns white in winter?

18 What are baby seals called?

19 Why does a glow-worm glow in the dark?

20 Redds are the breeding grounds of what?

21 What is a young pike called?

22 Where in the world do Britain's eels breed?

23 The natterjack is what kind of animal: bat, rat or toad?

24 Which is not a type of moth: leopard, lynx or tiger?

25 What kind of creature is a painted lady?

26 Why do gardeners appreciate the ladybird beetle?

27 What is a fox's tail called?

28 Which two animals appear on the royal coat of arms?

29 What is a female deer called?

30 Which part of England has no grey squirrels?

I CONFESS I'M SCARED.

Answers on page 217

Knowall's question:

What animal does the harpy eagle of South America, the world's biggest eagle, feed on?

FISH !!!

ASK ME ANOTHER

1 Which of the world's birds lays the largest eggs?

2 The biggest wingspan is found on which bird?

3 Which bird is the national emblem of the USA?

4 Arctic terns migrate: 12,000, 24,000 or 30,000 miles?

5 Which is the world's smallest bird?

6 Which species makes the nests for bird's nest soup?

7 On which island do birds of paradise live?

8 Why do some birds swallow grit?

9 Which little bird used to feature on the farthing coin?

10 What is the alternative name for a hedge sparrow?

11 Which bird is known as the sea parrot?

12 Which bird lays its eggs in another's nest?

13 In the USA they are chickadees. What are they here?

14 What is Britain's smallest bird?

15 What bird is the emblem of the RSPB?

16 Which flightless bird had a shoe polish named after it?

17 What is another name for the green plover?

18 From which birds were quills for writing usually taken?

19 "One for sorrow, two for joy". Which bird?

20 Which bird can hold three gallons of water in its bill?

21 What do Emperor penguins make their nests from?

22 How do male and female shelducks differ in appearance?

23 The English partridge is predominately what colour?

24 Which birds are kept at the Tower of London?

25 What African nation has a crane in the centre of its flag?

26 Sweden has which common bird as its national bird?

27 Which birds are still used to carry messages?

28 What bird flies majestically in the Andes Mountains?

29 Which notorious laughing bird is found in Australia?

30 *Geococcyx californias* is the Latin name for what bird?

YOU MAY LOSE YOUR APE-ITITE WHEN YOU HEAR THIS . . .

Answers on page 217

QUIZ NUMBER 53

Knowall's question:

What does the word dinosaur literally mean?

OLD BONES !!!

1 What kind of animals were the first vertebrates?

2 What is the study of fossils called?

3 Which was the fiercest carnivorous dinosaur?

4 What was the huge, now-extinct tiger noted for its teeth?

5 Diplodocus holds what distinction among dinosaurs?

6 What was the prehistoric equivalent of today's elephant?

7 What sort of creature was the coelacanth?

8 Kieselguhr is fossilised plankton. What is it used for?

9 Which was the heaviest dinosaur?

10 How many horns did the triceratops have?

11 What was special about a pterodactyl?

12 Where did plesiosaurs live?

13 What was the purpose of fins on some dinosaurs' backs?

14 Archaeopteryx linked which two kinds of animals?

15 In what geological epoch did the dinosaurs live?

16 Which fuel was formed during the Carboniferous period?

17 On what did oviraptosaurs live?

18 What was the name of Fred Flintstone's pet dinosaur?

19 Dinosaurs died out 35, 50, 65 or 80 million years ago?

20 What special feature did dimetrodon have?

21 Which massive animal had the smallest dinosaur brain?

22 What was the first dinosaur ever discovered?

23 In which county was Britain's biggest dinosaur find?

24 Where did iguanadon have pronounced bony spikes?

25 Name the spiral molluscs often found as fossils.

26 Of all dinosaurs, therizirosaurids had the largest what?

27 In what type of rocks are fossils found?

28 What was the giant legendary bird of the Sinbad stories?

29 There's a brisk trade in what dinosaur fossils?

30 In what geological period did true mammals appear?

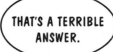

Answers on page 218

Knowall's question:

Which plants take their name from the Greek word for testicle?

COCONUTS !!!

1 Traditionally, cricket bats are made from which tree?

2 On which continent did the tobacco plant originate?

3 Name the pigment that makes leaves green.

4 What is the name for the simplest plants?

5 Which tree leaf appears on the Canadian flag?

6 What kind of plant is a hart's-tongue?

7 Which trees are found in many English churchyards?

8 The Colorado beetle attacks which common plant?

9 What kind of tree does cork come from?

10 Which tree is the favourite food of the koala bear?

11 The ointment calendula comes from which flower?

12 From which plant did Ancient Egyptians make paper?

13 What is the fastest growing plant?

14 Beech-mast contains what?

15 What is the upper layer of a tropical rainforest called?

16 What is another name for the mountain ash?

17 Rose hips are rich in which vitamin?

18 What is the fossilised resin of pine trees called?

19 The death-cap is the most poisonous type of what plant?

20 What kind of environment do halophytes thrive in?

21 In what way is the trunk of the cottonwood tree unusual?

22 What tree provides the beans for making chocolate?

23 Prickly pears are the fruit of what type of plant?

24 Which are the oldest living trees?

25 Which edible plant is picked from salt-marshes?

26 What vast Indian tree grows "trunks" from its branches?

27 What is the world's tallest species of tree?

28 What kind of tree do cobnuts come from?

29 Copra is the name for which dried tropical nut?

30 What is the national tree of Australia?

DON'T SHOUT
OR THE KIDS
WILL HEAR.

Answers on page 218

Knowall's question:

What plant is grown in paddy fields?

POTATOES !!!

1 What are Dame Edna Everage's favourite flowers?

2 What is the distinguishing characteristic of holm oaks?

3 Which synthetic fabric is made mainly from woodpulp?

4 Spagnum peat is formed by which kind of plant?

5 What plant gives Pernod its distinctive flavour?

6 What is the name of the main root of a tree?

7 Which flower is the emblem for the House of Lancaster?

8 What plant was the *Bounty's* cargo during the mutiny?

9 Saffron is harvested by hand from which flower?

10 The hyacinth is a member of which plant family?

11 Which plant was believed to scream when pulled up?

12 What are bents and fescues?

13 Which tree was decimated by a Dutch beetle?

14 What kinds of plants are Iceberg and Grandpa Dickson?

15 What plant is the national emblem of Scotland?

16 Which alcoholic drink is obtained from the agave plant?

17 The herb wild marjoram is usually known by what name?

18 In which continent did the leek originate?

19 What is the fertilising "powder" in plants called?

20 The juice of which fruit was used to combat scurvy?

21 Which flowers are represented by the *fleur-de-lys*?

22 Which gas is used to help ripen fruit?

23 What is the national flower of Wales?

24 What is the main food of reindeer and caribou?

25 Which palm plant has the world's largest leaves?

26 By what name is the plant convallaria better known?

27 Which plant could be either globe or Jerusalem?

28 Why is the polyanthus so called?

29 Aspidistras are pollinated by which creatures?

30 Which tree do silk worms feed on?

HE DOES HIS BEST TO CURRY FAVOUR.

Answers on page 218

QUIZ NUMBER 56

Knowall's question:

What is the correct nautical name for the upper edge of a ship's side?

THE RAILS !!!

1 How does a possum try to avoid attack or capture?

2 What value were the first two American stamps?

3 With what did the sparrow kill Cock Robin?

4 What nationality was the poet Henry Longfellow?

5 Who was Queen Victoria's favourite Highland ghillie?

6 On which river is England's highest waterfall?

7 Which work did Charles Dickens set partly in America?

8 What is the diameter of a basketball hoop?

9 What is the oldest type of winged insect?

10 Who is "mon ami" to ace detective Hercule Poirot?

11 What is the human tarsus?

12 Name the Muslim equivalent of the Red Cross.

13 What is the third planet in distance from the Sun?

14 Where did Drake's famous game of bowls take place?

15 What is signified by a Union flag flying upside-down?

16 How many noughts are there in a British billion?

17 What do sufferers of musophobia fear?

18 From which country does comic hero Tintin come?

19 What is the highest British decoration for civilians?

20 Name the disease abbreviated to MS.

21 Which playing card is known as "the Curse of Scotland"?

22 What effect does alcohol have on body temperature?

23 In translation, what capital means "Eastern city"?

24 Which king led the English at the Battle of Agincourt?

25 Who standardised the British screw thread in 1841?

26 By what name is the *Londonderry Air* better known?

27 Who was Elvis Presley's legendary manager?

28 What was the name of the first Rolls-Royce car?

29 What is a broad-pronged pickle fork called?

30 Which is the largest island in the Inner Hebrides?

THAT'S A
WHALE
OF A TALE.

Answers on page 218

Knowall's question:

Who wrote the play
The Quare Fellow?

JOE ORTON ???

1 Which one of the three Brontë sisters wrote the novel *Jane Eyre*?

2 What kind of snake does Cleopatra use to take her life in Shakespeare's *Antony and Cleopatra*?

3 What is the name of the principal character in Graham Greene's *Brighton Rock*?

4 Which poem by George Crabbe inspired Benjamin Britten's *Peter Grimes*?

5 Who wrote the tragedies *The White Devil* and *The Duchess of Malfi*?

6 Who is the hero of C. S. Forester's seafaring novels set during the Napoleonic Wars?

7 Name one of the three Dublin-born writers who have won the Nobel Prize for Literature.

8 In which 17th-century allegorical book does Christian make a pilgrimage, and who wrote it?

9 Which Leo Tolstoy novel tells the story of a married woman's passion for a young officer?

10 Whose adventures were the sequel to Mark Twain's *Tom Sawyer*?

11 What is the name of the child brought up by the elderly Silas Marner in George Eliot's book?

12 At which university was poet Philip Larkin a librarian for most of his working life?

13 Which character in Sheridan's *The Rivals* famously misapplies her words?

14 Who wrote a novel about a young Irish barrister called Phineas Finn?

15 Which L. P. Hartley novel recalls the events of a hot summer in 1900 at a large Norfolk country house?

16 To whom does Elizabeth Bennett become engaged in Jane Austen's *Pride and Prejudice*?

17 Who is the Booker Prize-winning sister of novelist Margaret Drabble?

18 Which novel features Captain Ahab and Ishmael, and which American wrote it?

19 Who will chiefly be remembered for his original tale of a vampire, and what is the book's title?

20 Which 19th-century children's author wrote the nonsense poem *The Hunting of the Snark*?

21 Which writer lived for many years in Rye, Sussex and became a British citizen a year before his death?

22 In which Oscar Wilde play does Lady Bracknell appear as a formidable aunt?

23 What is the ornithological title of Flora Thompson's autobiographical trilogy?

24 Which satirical book by Thomas Love Peacock takes place at a house party?

25 Which children's classic relates the life of a black horse, and who wrote it?

26 Who wrote *The Last of the Wine*, the first of eight books fictionalising life in Ancient Greece?

27 In which Oliver Goldsmith comedy does the character Tony Lumpkin appear?

28 Name two of the four March sisters in Louisa May Alcott's classic *Little Women*?

29 With which book did William Burroughs achieve cult status in 1959?

30 Michael Henchard is the leading character in which novel by Thomas Hardy?

THAT'S AN IRISH ANSWER IF EVER I HEARD ONE.

Answers on page 219

Knowall's question:

What did Aristotle describe as "the best provision for old age"?

A PENSION !!!

1 The title of which American novel has passed into the language to describe a "no-win" situation?

2 Name one of the two early Greek epics supposedly written by Homer.

3 Who travelled round England on horseback in the 19th century, and what collection of essays did he write?

4 What part of the English countryside provides the setting for R. D. Blackmore's *Lorna Doone*?

5 Who collaborated to write a series of stories that included *Some Experiences of an Irish R.M.*?

6 Which book by Jerome K. Jerome is a comic account of a fortnight on the river Thames?

7 Who was accompanied by his squire Sancho Panza in the satirical tale by Cervantes?

8 In which language did Irish playwright Samuel Beckett first write much of his work?

9 What is the name of the group of writers and painters that included Lytton Strachey and Virginia Woolf?

10 What is Hamlet's mother called in Shakespeare's play of the same name?

11 Which famous Scottish poet's birthday is celebrated on 25 January?

12 Which Russian writer described life in a labour camp in *One Day in the Life of Ivan Denisovich*?

13 Which Belgian writer created the pipe-smoking Paris detective Maigret?

14 What provides the background to most of Joseph Conrad's novels?

15 Which 19th-century poet wrote some 2,000 poems, only seven of which were published in her lifetime?

16 What is the title of the classic mythological trilogy by J. R. R. Tolkien?

17 Which work consists of 100 stories told by young people fleeing the plague?

18 Which 20th-century Welsh poet and playwright was married to the long-suffering Caitlin?

19 Which classic book is the story of a man shipwrecked on a desert island, and who wrote it?

20 Which character in Charles Dickens' *Martin Chuzzlewit* has provided an alternative name for an umbrella?

21 Which "Gothic tale of terror", told through the letters of an Arctic explorer, was written by Mary Shelley?

22 Which humorous American writer illustrated his stories with comic drawings of men, women, and dogs?

23 What was the first novel written by the 19th-century French author Gustave Flaubert?

24 Who wrote the adventures of the sporting Cockney grocer Jorrocks?

25 Which bird is shot in Coleridge's *The Rime of the Ancient Mariner*, causing a curse to fall on the ship?

26 Which outspoken Glaswegian author writes in the vernacular and was a controversial Booker winner?

27 Which 19th-century romantic Lakeland poet "wandered lonely as a cloud"?

28 What was the profession of the shipwrecked Gulliver in Jonathan Swift's *Gulliver's Travels*?

29 To which book does *The Miller's Tale* belong, and who wrote it?

30 Which American poet and playwright, living in London, wrote *Murder in the Cathedral*?

THERE'S A LESSON FOR US ALL.

Answers on page 219

Knowall's question:

Who wrote "to err is human, to forgive divine"?

THE POPE !!!

1 Which American playwright wrote *Death of a Salesman* and was married to Marilyn Monroe?

2 Who is the central male character in Emily Brontë's *Wuthering Heights*?

3 Which book by Charles Kingsley tells the story of Tom the chimney-sweep?

4 What is the name of the narrator and hero in Robert Louis Stevenson's *Treasure Island*?

5 Which Nobel Prize-winner wrote an Edwardian family saga, and what is its title?

6 What is the name of the child brought up by wolves in Rudyard Kipling's *The Jungle Book*?

7 Which novel by Boris Pasternak takes place during the Russian Revolution?

8 Novelist Winston Graham created a Cornish saga that featured which family?

9 Which Thackeray novel follows the fortunes of Becky Sharp and Amelia Sedley?

10 Whose 1962 best-selling novel *The Golden Notebook* was later acclaimed by feminists?

11 To whom does Mr Knightly propose in Jane Austen's novel *Emma*?

12 Which American novelist and short story writer wrote *Tanglewood Tales*?

13 Which poet wrote the lyrical drama in four acts, *Prometheus Unbound*?

14 Which poet and playwright writes about the importance of the culture of the West Indies?

15 Phileas Fogg undertook an epic circumnavigation of the globe in which Jules Verne novel?

16 What are the names of Gerald Durrell's brothers and sister who appear in *My Family and Other Animals*?

17 Who wrote and illustrated a collection of poems entitled *Songs of Innocence*?

18 What is the title of Jung Chang's book about China as seen through the eyes of three generations of women?

19 In which John Osborne play is angry young man Jimmy Porter the main character?

20 From whom does Antonio borrow some money in Shakespeare's *The Merchant of Venice*?

21 What is the title of Christina Rossetti's poem that tells the story of two sisters tempted with forbidden fruit?

22 Which satirist of university life lists his recreations as "none" in *Who's Who?*?

23 What is the title of the contemporary novel about a record collection, and who wrote it?

24 Which Sheffield-born novelist, travel writer and photographer died of Aids in 1989?

25 Which Czech-born playwright, originally Tom Straussler, wrote *Rosencrantz and Guildenstern Are Dead*?

26 What is the name of the girl brought up by Miss Havisham in Charles Dickens' *Great Expectations*?

27 Who began which bestselling novel in the 1950s while in a sanitorium recovering from TB?

28 Which television presenter and writer sets most of his novels in Cumbria?

29 Which poet wrote *Elegy Written in a Country Church-Yard* and *The Bard*?

30 The Robert Altman film *Short Cuts* was based on the short stories of which American writer?

NEAR MISS, KNOWALL.

Answers on page 219

Knowall's question:

Who did Sherlock Holmes regard as his superior in deductive powers?

DOCTOR WATSON !!!

1 Who sprang to instant publishing superstardom with the publication of *The Firm*?

2 In which novel did Ian Fleming's James Bond make his first appearance?

3 Which former television reporter and newsreader began his thriller-writing career with *Harry's Game*?

4 Name the ex-Marine, investment expert and friend of royalty who features in many of Tom Clancy's books?

5 In whose detective novels do Hercule Poirot and Miss Marple appear?

6 Which prolific British crime author also writes under the pen-name Barbara Vine?

7 Under what pseudonym does author Campbell Black write thrillers named after different dances?

8 Who is the put-upon hero of the *Game/Set/Match* and *Hook/Line/Sinker* trilogies by Len Deighton?

9 Which English-educated author returned to America and created wisecracking private eye Philip Marlowe?

10 The former profession of the "Queen Mother's favourite author" Dick Francis was what?

11 Which writer's Dirk Pitt is a master of the deep, and meets the author on the page from time to time?

12 Whose best-selling thriller *Enigma* was set in Britain's wartime codebreaking establishment at Bletchley Park?

13 Patricia Highsmith's "murderer, con man, forger and squire of a pleasant estate in France" was who?

14 Which Victorian author wrote classic detective stories *The Woman in White* and *The Moonstone*?

15 Which entrepreneur who founded *Today* newspaper began a thriller-writing career with *Ring of Red Roses*?

16 What author, married to Katharine Whitehorn, wrote about troubleshooter Major Harry Maxim?

17 Dorothy L. Sayers created which aristocratic detective and what long-suffering butler?

18 *The Guns of Navarone* and *Ice Station Zebra* were written by which Scottish adventure novelist?

19 Who is the American author who specialises in epic adventure novels set in Japan with titles like *The Ninja*?

20 Which writer created the medieval monk-investigator Brother Cadfael of Shrewsbury?

21 *The Amateur Cracksman* by E. W. Hornung introduced which gentleman burglar and leg-spin bowler?

22 Detective Inspector Morse and Sergeant Lewis were created by which writer living in Oxford?

23 *The Odessa File* was the second novel of which best-selling British author?

24 Virginia pathologist Doctor Kay Scarpetta is the lead character in crime novels by which writer?

25 What was the title of Richard Condon's novel, later a successful film, about two Mafia killers who fall in love?

26 What was the pen-name of Kenneth Millar, creator of tough California sleuth Lew Archer?

27 Which prolific British adventure novelist saw wartime service as a young anti-aircraft gunner?

28 Who creates the mysteries unravelled by Scotland Yard detective and poet Adam Dalgliesh?

29 What do the titles of many thrillers by author Craig Thomas have in common?

30 Which Belfast-born best-selling thriller writer once operated under the name Harry Patterson?

OH BROTHER.

Answers on page 219

Knowall's question:

Who wrote *A Hitch-Hiker's Guide to the Galaxy?*

NEIL ARMSTRONG !!!

1 What is the first name of Mary Shelley's tragic hero Baron Frankenstein?

2 Which film about a protean monster took inspiration from John W. Campbell's book *Who Goes There*?

3 What is the name of Captain Nemo's terrifying underwater dreadnought in the book by Jules Verne?

4 Which 16th-century astronomer wrote about a daring voyage to the moon in his work *Somnium*?

5 What is the title of the Arthur C. Clarke story which inspired the film *2001: A Space Odyssey*?

6 What is the name of the spacecraft once captained by James T. Kirk?

7 Who is the oppressed hero of George Orwell's hellish vision of the future, *1984*?

8 In which classic E. T. A. Hoffman story does a man fall in love with a machine?

9 What is the name of C. S. Lewis' magical realm that exists beyond a wardrobe?

10 In which E. R. Burroughs novel is an island in the South Pacific occupied by prehistoric monsters?

11 Which famous 19th-century designer wrote a series of novels about quasi-medieval worlds?

12 In *Star Wars*, what is the relationship between Darth Vader and Luke Skywalker?

13 Who wrote the classic sci-fi novel *The Time Machine*, in which the Eloi and the Morlocks appear?

14 What does Professor Challenger bring back from the "Lost World" to prove that it exists?

15 In which Fritz Lang film of 1926 do impoverished workers live beneath a city occupied by the wealthy?

16 Which doctor discovers a drug that concentrates evil in a novel by Robert Louis Stevenson?

17 What is the nationality of cult science fiction writer Stanislaw Lem?

18 To what does the *Fahrenheit 451* in Ray Bradbury's book title refer?

19 Which Russian-born American writer's first sci-fi novel was entitled *Pebble in the Sky*?

20 In which book of 1874 does Mor Jokai predict the advent of electrically powered flying machines?

21 Who played beautiful astronaut Barbarella in the 1960s adaptation of Jean-Claude Forest's book?

22 Which author, known for novels such as *Howards End*, wrote the short story *The Machine Stops*?

23 Who directed the radio adaptation of H. G. Wells' *The War of the Worlds* in 1938, causing panic in America?

24 Who wrote *The Chrysalids*, *The Midwich Cuckoos* and *The Kraken Wakes*?

25 In which important book by William Gibson does cyber cowboy Case appear?

26 What is the name of Flash Gordon's merciless enemy, and on which planet does he rule?

27 Can you name the valet who helps Phileas Fogg circumnavigate the world in 80 days?

28 In what mystical world do the adventures of Bilbo Baggins take place?

29 The Earth becomes a vast swamp in which of J. G. Ballard's "catastrophe" novels?

30 Which Margaret Atwood novel centres on Offred's life in The Republic of Gilead?

THE ANSWER'S AS OLD AS ADAM.

Answers on page 220

Knowall's question:

What flower painting by Vincent van Gogh fetched £28 million at auction in 1987?

SUNFLOWERS !!!

1 Name one of the two English artists who are the most famous painters of horses.

2 Which Italian painter noted for "red" canvasses died in Venice of the plague in 1576, aged about 99?

3 What was the name used by the successful painter son of Hans Holbein the Elder?

4 Which French artist is particularly known for paintings of dancers and women washing themselves?

5 Who was the artist and magazine illustrator famed for his sentimental portrayal of small-town American life?

6 Which eminent French sculptor created *The Thinker* and *The Kiss*?

7 What type of primitive art is associated with Les Combarelles in southern France?

8 What is the title of the famous painting of a stag by Victorian artist Sir Edwin Landseer?

9 French artist Seurat pioneered a method of painting that uses thousands of tiny dots. What is it called?

10 The mistress of which painter, knighted by Charles I, tried to bite off his thumb to stop his constant work?

11 What is the name of the medium of watercolour paint made opaque by the addition of white?

12 Which Dutchman known for *The Laughing Cavalier* was sued by a rival female artist for stealing her pupil?

13 Pictures exhibited in 1849 with the initials "PRB" were the work of which secret association of young artists?

14 What is the name for a religious picture created as an object of worship, often portraying virgin and child?

15 Which flamboyant French painter spent his last years in the South Seas and died in poverty?

16 Who painted the *Mona Lisa* and in which French gallery is it hung?

17 By what title is the great artistic movement meaning *la rinascita* in Italian more commonly known?

18 Which 16th-century Flemish master with two painter sons was notable for depicting scenes of peasant life?

19 What is the name given to a painting or carving on three adjacent panels?

20 Which Elizabethan painter is renowned for mastery of the miniature portrait?

21 Which artist, son of a dyer, painted the massive picture *Paradise* (84ft by 34ft) for the Doge of Venice?

22 Which major embroidered work chronicles the life of King Harold and the Norman Conquest of 1066?

23 In which Italian town are Giotto's famous frescoes in the Scrovegni chapel?

24 Which legendary Italian artist painted *The Birth of Venus* and *The Adoration of the Magi*?

25 What ceramic technique named after Majorca was developed by Moorish potters in the 16th century?

26 Name the Italian artist best known for his paintings of Venice, particularly the canals.

27 A great English artist's Christian names were Joseph Mallord William. Who was he?

28 Which artist, who lived at Giverny, painted *Impression – Sunrise*, which gave Impressionism its name?

29 Which 18th-century Suffolk-born landscape artist and portrait painter was a great rival to Joshua Reynolds?

30 Which humorous illustrator portrayed incredibly complex machines designed to do the simplest task?

IF YOU OPENED YOUR EYES YOU'D SEE THE ANSWER.

Answers on page 220

QUIZ NUMBER 63

Knowall's question:

For what subject matter
is the American painter
Audubon famous?

BEES !!!

1 Which great Italian master painted the ceiling of the Sistine Chapel in Rome?

2 Which Spanish artist went to Paris in 1900 and amazed fellow artists with his geometrically distorted forms?

3 What movement places emphasis on artists' emotions or inner vision above the importance of reality?

4 Which painter and engraver satirised London life with *The Harlot's Progress* and *The Rake's Progress*?

5 What was the nationality of 16th-century religious painter Hieronymous Bosch?

6 Which aristocratic late Victorian painter led the trend for sentimental classicism and idealism?

7 What is the term used to describe the decoration of religious texts, including initial letters?

8 Which English artist who died aged 26 in 1898 was a leading exponent of the decadence of *art nouveau*?

9 A 38m (125ft) tall sculpture of Christ by Paul Landowski done in 1931 stands above which South American city?

10 For what sort of illustrative technique is wildlife artist and chronicler of country life Thomas Bewick known?

11 Which Spanish painter was expelled from Europe's Surrealists for backing Franco in the Civil War?

12 Which great landscape artist who portrayed the idyll of rural England painted *The Hay Wain*?

13 What name is used to describe paintings traditionally made on walls coated in unset plaster?

14 The *fin de siècle* paintings and posters of which short, crippled French artist featured exotic Montmartre life?

15 Which English caricaturist is best known for his cartoons of the Napoleonic Wars period?

16 Which painter cut off part of his ear, sold only one picture in his lifetime and eventually killed himself?

17 Which famous 16th-century Spanish painter, whose name means "The Greek", was born in Crete?

18 A lost work by which artist confined to an asylum for killing his father was found on the *Antiques Roadshow*?

19 Which Yorkshire-born woman abstract sculptor was a fellow student of Henry Moore?

20 *The Snake Charmer* and *The Dream*, created by self-taught Henri Rousseau, are what type of paintings?

21 Which English society watercolourist is known for his Spanish gypsy subjects?

22 Greek antiquities including a frieze from the Parthenon were brought to Britain by which aristocrat in 1812?

23 Which master Dutch portrait painter (renowned for self-portraits) declared himself bankrupt in 1656?

24 Which major Impressionist painter had a son who became a prominent Hollywood film director?

25 J. L. David was closely linked with the French Revolution. Whose official painter did he become?

26 Which German painter and engraver created a book of woodcuts in 1498 entitled *The Apocalypse*?

27 For what are Tom Keating and Han van Meegeren known in the art world?

28 Which London art gallery completed in 1897 was paid for by the profits from sugar?

29 The 19th-century illustrator Phiz was associated with whose literary works?

30 Which ceramics firm with a reputation for top-quality wares was founded at Etruria, Staffordshire in 1760?

Answers on page 220

Knowall's question:

What controversial modern building dominates the waterfront in Sydney, Australia?

THE HARBOUR BRIDGE !!!

1 Which grim prison in Paris, symbol of the monarchy's authority, was stormed by the mob on 14 July 1789?

2 What is the official riverside London residence of the Archbishop of Canterbury?

3 Sir Winston Churchill lived at which house in Kent from 1922 to 1964?

4 What Scottish castle associated with the Queen Mother's family sheltered the Old Pretender in 1715?

5 Which great English country house did Nancy Astor, Britain's first woman MP, make a centre for society?

6 What great cathedral was completed in 1633, 120 years after the foundation stone was laid?

7 What is the name of the Royal Family's house and estate in the Scottish Highlands?

8 In 1818, John Nash remodelled the exterior of which seaside building in Mogul emperor style?

9 Which building in Berlin was burned by the Nazis in February 1933?

10 What 18th-century mill forms the centrepiece of the preserved industrial site at Styal Park, Cheshire?

11 Which perfectly concentric castle started in 1295 by Edward 1 is on the island of Anglesey?

12 What was Sir Christopher Wren's landmark building, started after London's Great Fire and finished in 1711?

13 Name the building alongside London's Waterloo Bridge once used as the Registry of Births, Marriages & Deaths.

14 Emperor Shahjahan's monument to his favourite wife was completed at Agra in 1653. What is it?

15 The Pompidou Centre in Paris and the Lloyds Building in London were designed by which British architect?

16 What well-preserved castle begun in 1078 with the White Tower remains a popular UK tourist attraction?

17 Which ruined English abbey stands on the spot where Joseph of Arimathea leaned on a staff which took root?

18 What soaring building forms the centrepiece of the London Docklands development started in the 1980s?

19 John Constable was brought up in – and later immortalised on canvas – which working building?

20 Which great Sikh religious shrine was completed at Amritsar in 1605?

21 What famous romantic novelist lived at the impressive Abbotsford House in the Scottish borders?

22 Which quirky Welsh village built by Clough Williams-Ellis appeared in cult TV programme *The Prisoner*?

23 The 16th-century Lindisfarne Castle on Holy Island is off the coast of which English county?

24 Two of the buildings of St John's College, Cambridge are linked by what famous structure?

25 Blenheim Palace in Oxfordshire is the home of which ducal family ennobled as a result of military success?

26 The Nutshell, leading claimant as Britain's smallest pub, is in which West Suffolk town?

27 What building opened in London's Bloomsbury in 1759 to serve as "a repository for arts and sciences"?

28 In 1682, the largest palace in Europe was completed for French King Louis XIV. Where is it located?

29 Which German architect designed the severe Seagram Building in New York and famously said "less is more"?

30 Which fortress in Peking was the site of the Chinese emperors' palaces from 1421?

JUST AS WELL HE DOESN'T HAVE TO SING FOR HIS SUPPER.

Answers on page 220

QUIZ NUMBER 65

Knowall's question:

What simply designed camera brought photography to the masses from 1900?

THE CAMCORDER !!!

1 Which British design guru founded the Habitat store chain in 1964?

2 Who was the American master of decorative *art nouveau* glass, especially lamps?

3 Which German school of arts, crafts and industrial design was founded in 1919 by Walter Gropius?

4 What was the first mass-produced British car to be designed by Alec Issigonis?

5 Which French firm famous for luxury jewellery and timepieces designed the first wrist watch in 1904?

6 The world's first refrigerator was designed by German Karl von Linde in: 1876, 1886, 1896, 1906 or 1916?

7 Which influential Swiss architect, designer and town planner wrote *Towards a New Architecture*?

8 Queen Elizabeth II's dressmaker also designed wartime utility clothing and uniforms. What was his name?

9 Who designed the Bouncing Bomb used in the 1943 Dambuster raids on Germany's Möhne and Eder dams?

10 The Glasgow School of Art and Cranston Tea Rooms were designed by which Scottish artist and architect?

11 Which British ceramics decorator and designer was responsible for colourful *art deco* "Bizarre" pottery?

12 The Cenotaph memorial in Whitehall was created by the architect who designed much of New Delhi. Who?

13 American industrial designer Raymond Loewy designed a classic pack for which brand of cigarettes in 1940?

14 In 1892, which German designed the compression combustion engine which bears his name to this day?

15 Which flexible office desk lamp was designed by Briton George Carwardine in 1934?

16   When did a tractor with an internal combustion engine first appear: 1879, 1889, 1899, 1909 or 1919?

17   The prototype of which strikingly designed supersonic airliner made its maiden flight in 1969?

18   In 1947, Italian helicopter designer D'Ascanio devised which motor scooter that became a classic?

19   What French firm became famous in the early 1900s for glassware, including scent bottles and car mascots?

20   Which transport map, largely unchanged to the present, was designed by Harry Beck in 1933?

21   Which American brothers designed and produced the first successful powered airplane in 1903?

22   Name the Japanese motor-cycle manufacturer who introduced the classically styled Gold Wing in 1989.

23   Which British typographical designer produced, among many other typefaces, Gill Sans?

24   In 1915, which Swedish electrical goods manufacturer perfected the horizonal cylinder vacuum cleaner?

25   Which Barcelona architect designed many distinctive buildings, including the Church of the Sagrada Familia?

26   In 1930, who designed the Volkswagen Beetle, which became the most popular car ever produced?

27   Which British clothing and furnishing designer started a chain of stores based on romantic country designs?

28   The high profile but unsuccessful C5 electric car was designed by which British inventor and innovator?

29   Italian architect Marcello Nizzoli designed a range of typewriters for which company?

30   Which eminent British designer established the Kelmscott Press in 1891?

HE SHOULD START TRAINING FOR THE GIRL GUIDES.

Answers on page 221

QUIZ NUMBER 66

Knowall's question:

For how long did the
Hundred Years' War last:
86, 96, 100, 106?

ONE HUNDRED !!!

1 Which is the oldest underground system in the world:
Budapest, London, New York, Paris?

2 Which was the first underground line to open in London:
Circle, District, Metropolitan, Piccadilly?

3 Which is Shakespeare's longest play:
Hamlet, Henry V, Othello, Richard III?

4 Which is the oldest university in the UK:
Cambridge, Durham, Oxford, St Andrews?

5 Which one of these cheeses comes from Switzerland:
Feta, Gruyère, Parmesan, Roquefort?

6 What is the major art gallery in Madrid called:
The Louvre, the Prado, the Rijksmuseum, the Uffizi?

7 Which is the oldest cathedral in the UK:
Canterbury, Lincoln, Winchester, York?

8 Who was the first Roman emperor:
Augustus, Claudius, Julius Caesar, Nero?

9 Which British monarch has reigned the longest:
Henry III, Elizabeth I, George III, Victoria?

10 Who was the youngest British monarch:
Edward III, Richard II, Henry VI, Victoria?

11 Who was the oldest British king to ascend the throne:
William I, James II, George I, William IV?

12 Who was the oldest serving British prime minister:
Churchill, Disraeli, Gladstone, Palmerston?

13 Which one of the following is a Roman god:
Apollo, Mercury, Pan, Zeus?

14 Which organisation has the largest UK membership:
Automobile Association, National Trust, RSPB, UNISON?

15 In Britain which month is most popular for marriage:
May, June, July, August?

16 Which is the nearest city to London:
Birmingham, Bristol, Gloucester, Norwich?

17 In which war was the concentration camp introduced:
Boer War, Crimean War, World War 1, World War 2?

18 What number does the Roman numeral D represent:
250, 300, 500, 750?

19 What was the most popular film of the 1940s:
Bambi, Cinderella, Fantasia, Pinocchio?

20 Which language has most speakers in the world:
English, Hindustani, Mandarin Chinese, Spanish?

21 Which country has the most French speakers:
Algeria, Canada, France, Morocco?

22 Which country was first to ratify the UN charter:
Chile, France, Nicaragua, USA?

23 Which country was first to give women the vote:
Canada, Finland, Netherlands, New Zealand?

24 Which one of the following is a cinque port:
Dover, Lowestoft, Southampton, Weymouth?

25 Who was the first Pope:
Anacletus, Clement I, Linus, Peter?

26 Who was the oldest US president at inauguration:
Bush, Eisenhower, Reagan, Truman?

27 Which king came first:
Ethelbald, Ethelbert, Ethelred, Ethelwulf?

28 Which fresh fruits have the fewest calories per 100g:
bananas, cherries, peaches, strawberries?

29 Which disease has the shortest incubation period:
chickenpox, diphtheria, mumps, whooping cough?

30 Which is the largest wind instrument:
bassoon, clarinet, cor anglais, oboe?

HE'S FEELING LOW.

Answers on page 221

Knowall's question:

Which actress is the wife of TV playwright Jack Rosenthal of *London's Burning* fame?

MIRIAM KARLIN !!!

TRIVIA KING

1 Name the two FBI special agents who battle against the forces of the unknown in *The X-Files*.

2 Who stars as ex-Crusader and investigative monk Brother Cadfael of Shrewsbury?

3 Which presenter became famous for his long-running *The Sky at Night* series?

4 Which characters were played by Dudley Sutton and Phyllis Logan in *Lovejoy*?

5 Name the western drama featuring an epic cattle drive starring Robert Duvall and Tommy Lee Jones.

6 Magnus Magnusson is the firm but fair presenter of which long-running programme?

7 Whose whispered delivery has become a hallmark of BBC wildlife programmes over the years?

8 Which 1970s drama was co-created by Jean Marsh, who also appeared in the series as Rose?

9 Name the largely silent purveyor of disaster created by Rowan Atkinson.

10 Which acclaimed presenter of *Gardeners' World* died suddenly in 1996?

11 What late-night show was introduced by ITV to serve addicts of the newly arrived Internet?

12 Who is the film expert and writer who fronts the BBC's long-running movie review programme?

13 In which hard-hitting northern police drama do DC Warren Allen and DC Marty Brazil feature?

14 Who, in the 1966 Christmas edition of *Not Only . . . But Also*, appeared as Dan the gents toilet commissionaire?

15 In the very first episode of *Star Trek*, what was the USS *Enterprise* flying?

16 Which elegant former England batsman hosts a television cricketing programme?

17 Name the genial Australian TV personality who made a brief cameo appearance as a postman in *Neighbours*.

18 Which cultured ex-Liverpool defender has become an outspoken summariser on BBC soccer programmes?

19 What BBC programme has been presented by Robert Robinson, Kenneth Robinson and Anne Robinson?

20 Terry Wogan hosted which programme featuring a selection of unfortunate sporting happenings?

21 What powerful US hospital drama features doctors Jeffrey Geiger, Aaron Shutt and Dennis Hancock?

22 Which US series featuring the characters Leland McKenzie and Arnie Becker switched to Sky in 1992?

23 Name the lollipop-sucking, bald New York cop who was portrayed by Telly Savalas in the 1970s.

24 Which footballer was the inspiration for international soccer star Darren Matthews in *All in the Game*?

25 Who broke a personal rule never to play the same character twice in political drama *To Play the King*?

26 Which long-running Granada show hosted by Bamber Gascoigne was revived on the BBC in the 1990s?

27 What US comedy drama has an all-star female cast including Dolly Parton and Shirley MacLaine?

28 Who first presented *The Big, Big Talent Show* in which viewers vote by telephone?

29 Name the dry-ice wreathed astrologer who quickly became a feature on *The National Lottery Live*.

30 Whose government axe hangs over the working lives of Jack, Ethel, Cecil and May?

BEAT THAT – HIS LIPS NEVER MOVED.

Answers on page 221

Knowall's question:

What 1970s children's TV programme took its name from the phrase "This Is Saturday Wear A Smile"?

WATCH WITH MOTHER !!!

1 Which UK soap has topped the viewing ratings more times than any other programme?

2 Ian Hislop and Paul Merton were the regular panellists on which satirical current affairs programme?

3 Sharon Maughan and Anthony Head developed their TV romance over a cup or two of what?

4 In 1995, which supposedly light-hearted programme was rapped for "increasingly obvious sexual innuendo"?

5 What was the collective TV comedy name for Tim Brooke-Taylor, Bill Oddie and Graeme Garden?

6 What newly available film role did Patrick McGoohan, TV's *Danger Man* in the 1960s, famously turn down?

7 When did TV first bring the terrible plight of starving Ethiopians to the world: 1981, 1984, 1987, 1989?

8 Fluck and Law created which satirical programme that poked merciless puppet fun at anyone who moved?

9 Name the real-life husband and wife team who starred in the rustic drama *Forever Green*.

10 "Come on down" was the catchphrase of which TV host in which all-action game show?

11 What tough drama by Kay Mellor featured life, love and death among a group of prostitutes?

12 What Sunday programme topped the viewing ratings in the first full month of ITV's operations, October 1955?

13 Four acting Liverpool brothers are Joe, Paul, Mark and Stephen. What is their surname?

14 *Heartbeat* was a minor 1986 hit record for which *Miami Vice* heart-throb actor?

15 Sean Bean's wife Melanie Hill starred as the leading man's sister in which two 1994 Geordie dramas?

16 In which 1960s drama did Ryan O'Neal and Mia Farrow star as Rodney Harrington and Allison Mackenzie?

17 What manic half-hour hospital show penned by junior doctor John MacUre made its debut in 1994?

18 Which TV mogul once announced: "All my shows are great. Some of them are bad. But they are all great."?

19 In 1996, which slick soap set in the USA's Deep South marked the return of *Dynasty* creator Aaron Spelling?

20 Which major and captain married in the fourth series of *Soldier, Soldier*?

21 Name the reporter who had the scoop of 1995 with his *Panorama* interview of the Princess of Wales?

22 Who hosted *The Big Breakfast* before hitting the waiting world with *Don't Forget Your Toothbrush*?

23 Which high-tech thriller series debuted in 1995 with Craig McLachlan, Jessie Birdsall and Jaye Griffiths?

24 Name the comedian with the snappy catchphrase "loadsamoney" who got his own series in 1990.

25 Which 1975 cop drama featuring Regan, Carter and DI Haskins ran for 52 episodes in three years?

26 In 1995, which TV personality vanished after walking out of a play in which he starred with Rik Mayall?

27 Which puppet show, revived in 1996, once claimed to be the most-watched television series in the world?

28 In 1995, who won a £1 million contract to promote Estée Lauder products on TV and elsewhere?

29 What soap featuring the lives and loves of East End market folk first appeared in 1967?

30 What is the significance in television terms of these numbers: 3, 5, 14, 22, 30, 44, 10?

WAS HE WRONG OR WAS HE WRONG?

Answers on page 221

Knowall's question:

Which 1959 American western series about a cattle drive gave Clint Eastwood his first starring role?

BONANZA !!!

1 Robert Carlyle tirelessly patrols the Highland village of Lochdubh. What character does he play?

2 At which country house is Noel's House Party set, and who became the show's larger-than-life star?

3 The BBC's 1993 mega-flop *A Year in Provence* was based on the best-selling book by which writer?

4 What pioneering 1960s drama starring Carol White and Ray Brooks dealt with the plight of a homeless mum?

5 Which brothers are seen on television respectively reading national news and starring as Hercule Poirot?

6 In what year did *Hawaii Five-O* starring Jack Lord first appear: 1964, 1967, 1970, 1973 or 1976?

7 Singer Boy George made his American TV debut starring as who in an episode of *The A-Team*?

8 In which sitcom did Penelope Keith star as upper-class Audrey with Peter Bowles as *nouveau riche* Richard?

9 Alec Guinness played which shrewd spycatcher in John Le Carré's *Tinker, Tailor, Soldier, Spy*?

10 The postponement of final episodes of what 23-part courtroom drama caused a storm of protest in 1996?

11 What pale imitation of *Charlie's Angels* starred Jill Gascoigne, Rosalyn Landor and Leslie Ash?

12 In what comedy series did Kevin Whately get his big break as drippy Neville?

13 Name the creator of characters Captain Kremmen and biker Sid Snot, who died of Aids in 1995.

14 The "Top TV Ad" of 1986 starred Linda Bellingham as mum and Michael Redfern as dad of what family?

15 Who said in the early days of commercial television: "It's a licence to print money."?

16 Who played the hairnetted battleaxe Ena Sharples in *Coronation Street*?

17 Which TV and film actor first popped up in British Telecom ads in 1994 with the "it's good to talk" slogan?

18 Name the one original cast member to remain when *Brookside* celebrated its 10th birthday.

19 What popular series featuring a Scottish detective began life as a one-off three-part thriller called *Killer*?

20 The actor who played Peter "Tucker" Jenkins in *Grange Hill* went on to play which character in *EastEnders*?

21 In 1964, which former Radio Luxembourg DJ was the very first presenter of *Top of the Pops*?

22 Name the sly family whose cowardly dealings spanned the centuries from Elizabeth I to World War 1.

23 What cult 1960s children's puppet show reappeared on Channel 4 in 1992 with Nigel Planer's voiceover?

24 Which American cartoon series depicted 1960s lifestyles in a Stone Age setting?

25 Who admitted to Jonathan Dimbleby that he committed adultery after his marrriage had broken down?

26 Which long-running sitcom featured three elderly friends who forever indulged in childish pranks?

27 Who played Maddie Hayes and David Addison in the offbeat American detective series *Moonlighting*?

28 Name the "two Davids" who have been the only presenters of the BBC's *A Question of Sport*.

29 Who starred in the comedy series dealing with the ups and downs of *The Vicar of Dibley*?

30 In the 1960s, which ITV programme first tried hidden camera stunts played on the public?

ROWDY GETS A RAW DEAL.

Answers on page 221

Knowall's question:

Who actually *did* shoot JR in that eagerly awaited *Dallas* denouément?

SUE ELLEN !!!

1 What hyped but ill-fated BBC "soap for Europe" sank without trace in 1993?

2 What is the surname of Del Boy, Rodney, Grandad and Uncle Albert in *Only Fools and Horses*?

3 Which sitcom featuring three female generations of one family transferred from radio to TV in 1988?

4 What leading Australian soap role has been played by actresses Vanessa Downing and Debra Lawrance?

5 What is the name of the disembodied hand kept in a box by *The Addams Family*?

6 Which comedy starring Martin Clunes switched from ITV to the BBC after two series?

7 What is the full name of the manic character played by Jennifer Saunders in *Absolutely Fabulous*?

8 One of the youngest members of the *Dad's Army* cast died in 1973. Who was he?

9 How many series of the classic John Cleese sitcom *Fawlty Towers* were made?

10 In *Taxi*, who played the vicious, lecherous, pint-sized dispatcher of the Sunshine Cab Company?

11 Cliff Richard sang the theme song of which horsey BBC soap which galloped into the sunset in 1992?

12 Which sitcom features the last survivor on a mining spaceship destined to roam the cosmos for ever?

13 What was the bar owned by Ted Danson, who portrayed ex-Boston Red Sox pitcher Sam "Mayday" Malone?

14 Who played leading character Meg in the long-running soap *Crossroads*, which finally ended in 1988?

15 What 1980s series featuring boats and boardrooms was described as "the first Thatcherite soap"?

16. Who played Sidney Balmoral James in the 1960s sitcom *Citizen James*?

17. Which three surnames did the Joan Collins character Alexis have in *Dynasty*?

18. In what long-running American sitcom did Buddy Ebsen play patriarch Jed Clampett?

19. Which elderly sitcom character is reduced to shouting "I don't believe it!" at regular intervals?

20. What shattering contribution did the character James Willmott-Brown make to the plot of *EastEnders*?

21. What was the name of Arkwright's hapless nephew in *Open All Hours*?

22. In what comedy may cocky but accident-prone reporter Damien Day be found chasing a story?

23. Andrew Burt and Clive Hornby have both played which character in *Emmerdale*?

24. In which Melbourne prison may female prisoners be found in *Cell Block H*?

25. By what two names has the actress who plays *Roseanne* been known since the show began in 1989?

26. What gritty hour-long police drama turned into a gritty twice-weekly police soap?

27. Which actor played Rigsby in *Rising Damp* and Reggie Perrin in *The Fall and Rise of Reginald Perrin*?

28. Name the Australian production company responsible for creating *Neighbours*.

29. Which *EastEnders* star went north and turned up as a 1960s copper in *Heartbeat*?

30. Which ageing Hollywood star played clan leader Jason Colby in *Dynasty* spin-off *The Colbys*?

THE GUY REALLY IS A BIT OF A SISSY.

Answers on page 222

Knowall's question:

What distinctive type of car did Jersey detective Jim Bergerac drive?

A POLICE CAR !!!

1 Name the versatile actor who plays moody, George Cross-winning DI "Jack" Frost of Denton police.

2 Which writer created *Widows* and the enormously successful *Prime Suspect* for television?

3 Stratford Johns played Detective Chief Inspector Charlie Barlow in which long-running 1960s TV series?

4 Who starred as Kingsmarkham policeman Reg and married on-screen wife Dora in real life?

5 Which short-lived police corruption drama was based on a film of the same name starring Al Pacino?

6 Patrick Malahyde appeared in *The Singing Detective* and what series based on Dame Ngaio Marsh's books?

7 Ex-pop singer Adam Faith starred as which Cockney spiv in ITV's 1971–72 comedy crime drama?

8 Which renowned barrister writer created irascible Horace Rumpole of the Bailey?

9 Which series of short murder mysteries fronted by "The Master of Suspense" ran to over 300 episodes?

10 After playing bit parts for years, which innovative cop series gave Daniel J. Travanti his big break in 1981?

11 What gritty black-and-white drama aired in the UK from 1966 starred Robert Stack as T-man Eliot Ness?

12 Which ex-horror actor was the man in charge of D-3, the Department of Queer Complaints at Scotland Yard?

13 A Glasgow detective series survived the death of its main character, DI Taggart. Who played him?

14 In *Cracker*, what was the full name of the larger-than-life character played by Robbie Coltrane?

15 What low-key 1990s police detective series starring Jack Shepherd is set in Cornwall?

16 Radio West is now a genuine radio station – but its fictional predecessor was home to which "private ear"?

17 Name the Dutch cop played by Barry Foster in widely-spaced series, in 1972, 1977 and 1991.

18 Which Chicago-based Catholic priest played by Tom Bosley had a God-given talent for solving mysteries?

19 Jasper Carrott and Robert Powell play which pair of gormless plainclothes detectives?

20 Which down-to-earth BBC series featuring a London copper of the old school ran from 1955 to 1976?

21 Where did ex-police clerk John Bird and newly retired policeman Alfred Molina head for in the yacht *El C.I.D.*?

22 In which crime series did Leslie Grantham and Don Henderson play "bad guy" and "good guy" brothers?

23 Who was on-the-run hero Dr Richard Kimble himself chasing in the 1960s drama *The Fugitive*?

24 What two characters – a lawyer and wheelchair-bound cop – did Raymond Burr play in successive TV series?

25 Name the actors who starred as Oxford detectives Morse and Lewis in *Inspector Morse*.

26 Which tough crime fighter was played by Edward Woodward in *The Equalizer*?

27 Deceptively bumbling police detective Lieutenant Columbo has a basset hound. What is its name?

28 Name the ex-Star Trekker who played the old cop who teaches young cops the ropes in *T. J. Hooker*.

29 What surreal David Lynch crime drama-cum-soap-opera was set in the USA's Pacific North-West?

30 Which soon-to-be-famous TV actor starred in a tough drama based on Heathrow's Brinks-Mat gold robbery?

AND HE HAS THE NERVE TO LOOK TRIUMPHANT.

Answers on page 222

QUIZ NUMBER 72

Knowall's question:

Who played a superb baddie in *Die Hard* and *Robin Hood: Prince of Thieves?*

JIMMY CAGNEY !!!

1 Which actor spoke the dreaded words "I'm going to make him an offer he can't refuse."?

2 Julie Andrews won an Oscar for her first film part in what wholesome 1964 movie?

3 Anne Bancroft played which character who seduced Dustin Hoffman in *The Graduate*?

4 Name the cartoon duo who devised the much-loved *Tom and Jerry* series of short films.

5 *A Hard Day's Night, Help!* and *Yellow Submarine* were three of the Beatles' films. What was the fourth?

6 The musical *Funny Girl* was a biopic of Ziegfield Follies singer Fanny Brice. Who played her?

7 Name Disney's 1996 film based on a Victor Hugo book about a lonely outsider.

8 Who made his acting reputation in *Trading Places* and *Beverly Hills Cop*?

9 What 1962 psychological thriller starring Gregory Peck and Robert Mitchum was remade in 1991?

10 What 1982 Ridley Scott cult movie starred Harrison Ford as a futuristic cop hunting renegade cyborgs?

11 In what film was Steve McQueen a bored tycoon who robbed banks and Faye Dunaway the investigator?

12 *Per un Pugno di Dollari* was the original title of which Sergio Leone western?

13 Which respected British actor played ailing composer Von Aschenbach in *Death in Venice*?

14 The Oscar-winning score for *Butch Cassidy and the Sundance Kid* was written by which composer?

15 Which rugby league tale directed by Lindsay Anderson in 1963 launched the career of Richard Harris?

16 Name the British director responsible for *10 Rillington Place*, *Gandhi* and *Cry Freedom*.

17 In what action thriller does Tom Cruise play a spy accused of spying on his fellow spies?

18 Which anarchic television comedy team created the films *The Life of Brian* and *The Meaning of Life*?

19 Which 1982 Spielberg sci-fi classic tells the story of an alien befriended by a small boy in Los Angeles?

20 In 1939, director John Ford made which classic western set largely in Monument Valley?

21 Which French composer wrote four film scores for David Lean, including *Doctor Zhivago*?

22 Who co-produced, directed and played the leading role in the Oscar-winning *Dances With Wolves*?

23 In which 1949 movie set in Vienna did Broadway colleagues Orson Welles and Joseph Cotten star?

24 In *The Sting*, which pairing of famous actors repeated earlier success playing two notorious outlaws?

25 Critic Alexander Walker called which weepie starring Ryan O'Neal and Ali MacGraw "*Camille* with bullshit"?

26 Who is the actor son of the Canadian-born star of *Klute* and *Don't Look Now*?

27 Which American born in 1963 made his directorial debut with the violent *Reservoir Dogs*?

28 In what early James Bond film did Sean Connery play the hero and Gert Frobe the baddie?

29 Australian actress Judith Anderson played what sinister role in Hitchcock's 1940 film *Rebecca*?

30 "Louis, I think this is the start of a beautiful friendship" were the last words of which classic 1942 film?

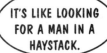

IT'S LIKE LOOKING FOR A MAN IN A HAYSTACK.

Answers on page 222

QUIZ NUMBER 73

Knowall's question:

Which cult 1970s book, featuring a bird who wanted to fly faster and find a perfect world, bombed as a film?

THE BIRDS !!!

1 Which two outlaws cut a swathe through America's 1930s Midwest in "the film event" of 1967?

2 What controversial 1996 movie featured a group of drug-taking misfits in Edinburgh?

3 Which British playwright won screenwriting Oscars for *Dr Zhivago* and *A Man For All Seasons*?

4 What 1980s car-chase comedy starred John Belushi and Dan Ackroyd as two unlikely soul artists?

5 Charlton Heston played Moses in which Cecil B. De Mille Old Testament epic?

6 *Out of Africa* and *White Mischief* were both set in which East African country?

7 What cult comedy film, later a TV series, was set in a mobile army hospital during the Korean War?

8 In what soulful 1935 adaptation of an epic Tolstoy novel did Greta Garbo play the title role?

9 Which actress starred opposite Michael Douglas as the bisexual millionairess in *Basic Instinct*?

10 What film about tourists acting out Christ's life was called "one of the true fiascos of modern cinema"?

11 In what 1955 Rodgers and Hammerstein musical does a cowboy win his girl against all the odds?

12 What 1991 best film starring Anthony Hopkins and Jodie Foster featured Hannibal "The Cannibal" Lecter?

13 Who starred in the adaptations of the Philip Roth books *Goodbye, Columbus* and *Portnoy's Complaint*?

14 Alan Bates played which character in the 1967 film version of Hardy's *Far From the Madding Crowd*?

15 The 1930s director and choreographer Busby Berkeley specialised in what?

16 Which film featuring the Battle of Rorke's Drift in 1879 gave Michael Caine his big screen break?

17 Name the Italian director who made *Last Tango in Paris* and *The Last Emperor*.

18 What movie featured World War 2 British prisoners on the Burma railway under stiff CO Alec Guinness?

19 Which 1963 film featuring English schoolboys on a desert island was remade in 1990 with American kids?

20 In *Capricorn One*, who plays the shambolic reporter who discovers that the first Mars mission is a hoax?

21 What thrice-made weepie's latest appearance in 1994 starred Warren Beatty and wife Annette Bening?

22 In which 1973 film is a girl possessed by evil, becoming a lethal monster before she is finally cured?

23 Which incongruous pairing starred in the enormously successful *Lethal Weapon* series?

24 What Hitchcock classic features a motel and vicious murders attributed to the young owner's mad mother?

25 Which Disney cartoon featured Elton John/Tim Rice songs and was the highest-grossing film of 1994?

26 What classic 1925 Russian silent film dealt with the naval mutiny at Odessa in 1905?

27 Name the Ealing comedy in which the people of Pimlico declare independence from the rest of Britain.

28 In what film do chalk-and-cheese couple Redford and Streisand marry, then change with the times?

29 The catchy music of films like *The Magnificent Seven* and *The Great Escape* was written by which composer?

30 Name the director of classic British films like *The Importance of Being Earnest* who was the son of an earl.

HE'S GULLIBLE WHEN IT COMES TO ORNITHOLOGY.

Answers on page 223

Knowall's question:

Which comedy actor starred in *The Pink Panther?*

INSPECTOR CLOUSEAU !!!

1 Who said to Bogey: "You know how to whistle, don't you, Steve? You just put your lips together and blow."?

2 American actress Jamie Lee Curtis is the daughter of which famous parents?

3 The best-known recluse in history directed the costly aviation epic *Hell's Angels* in 1930. Who was he?

4 Caryn Johnson is Hollywood's most successful African-American actress. What is her stage name?

5 For which film did Jessica Tandy win an Oscar at the ripe old age of 80 in 1989?

6 Name the famous dancer whose screen test report was: "Can't act. Slightly bald. Can dance a little."?

7 Who founded the Industrial Light & Magic special effects factory and directed *Star Wars*?

8 Name the former basketball player and professional acrobat who played the *Birdman of Alcatraz*?

9 Which actor was the grandfather of the author whose best-selling book inspired the film *Jaws*?

10 Name the mumbling "Master of the Method" who purchased an island near Tahiti in the 1960s.

11 Which producer-director twins made many British films including *Lucky Jim* and *I'm All Right Jack*?

12 Which one of the five performing Marx Brothers never appeared in any of their films?

13 In 1969, 34 years after she appeared in the film *Curly Top*, who became the US representative at the UN?

14 In a long career Mel Blanc contributed to over 3,000 short films. What was his speciality?

15 Which disillusioned swashbuckler remarked "The rest of my life will be devoted to women and litigation."?

16 Which great's first on-screen words were: "Water? Do I need it. I've had to shoot my horse."?

17 Name the actress who lost a multi-million dollar lawsuit after pulling out of the 1993 movie *Boxing Helena*.

18 Which naive simpleton progressing through American history won an Oscar for Tom Hanks in 1994?

19 What is Irving Berlin's all-time best-selling song, first sung by Bing Crosby in *Holiday Inn*.

20 Which perfectionist who started as a photographer on *Look* magazine directed *A Clockwork Orange*?

21 The American silent comic actor Roscoe Arbuckle was better known by what nickname?

22 Who did the voice of Mickey in the first Mickey Mouse "talkie", *Steamboat Willie* in 1928?

23 Whose death at the wheel of a speeding Porsche in 1955 ensured him screen immortality and cult status?

24 Composer Mikis Theodorakis wrote the zesty music for which 1964 film starring Anthony Quinn?

25 Which gap-toothed British comedy actor with an upper-crust voice died of Parkinson's disease in 1990?

26 Name the two 1930s stars who revived their careers in *Whatever Happened to Baby Jane* in 1962.

27 Which director who won an Oscar for *The Great McGinty* in 1940 offered to direct the film for $10?

28 In 1949, which beauty shocked the world by leaving her husband and child for director Roberto Rossellini?

29 Which hoofer, born Virginia McMath in 1911, found fame dancing opposite Fred Astaire in the 1930s?

30 "Tomorrow is another day" were the last words in what film, and which actress spoke them?

HE'LL NEVER SELL ME ON THE IDEA.

Answers on page 223

Knowall's question:

Which sensational platinum blonde actress arrived in Hollywood aged 16, already married?

MARILYN MONROE !!!

1 Whose self-conscious New York Jewish angst was reflected to good effect in Oscar-winning *Annie Hall*?

2 Which actress was born in Hawaii, raised in Australia, appeared nude in *Dead Calm* and lives with Tom Cruise?

3 Mack Sennett was "the king of silent comedy". What leading early Hollywood studio did he found?

4 The wife of which diminutive Polish film director was murdered by the "Manson Family" in 1969?

5 Name the fabled Hollywood hellraiser and ladies man who starred as The Joker in the 1989 film *Batman*.

6 Until she died, which star partnered Diana Hyland, who played his mother in *The Boy in the Plastic Bubble*?

7 Ex-Marine Gene Hackman won his first Oscar for the role of determined cop Popeye Doyle in what film?

8 Which puppeteer started on the TV show *Sam and his Friends* and later made the hit film *The Muppet Movie*?

9 Who was described as the "Eighth Wonder of the World" and terrorised New York City in 1933?

10 James Bond movie producer Albert R. Broccoli was known by what nickname?

11 Name two of the three actor sons of top Hollywood character player John Carradine.

12 Who took the title role in *Lawrence of Arabia* in 1962 after Albert Finney turned it down?

13 Which respected black actor was appointed president of Walt Disney in 1994?

14 Who said: "I'm no great actor and no great rider and no great singer. But whatever it is I'm doing they like it."

15 Which French actress won her country's Legion d'Honneur for services to acting and animal welfare?

16 Which clan consisted of stage-acting parents plus sons-and-daughter movie stars John, Lionel and Ethel?

17 Name the Broadway romantic lead who later became famous for horror films like *The Pit and the Pendulum*.

18 Which 10-year-old Oscar winner, daughter of a famous actor, later married tennis star John McEnroe?

19 In what 1959 movie did Jack Lemmon and Tony Curtis famously disguise themselves as women?

20 Which father-and-son martial arts actors both died young at the age of 33?

21 US actress and singer Cherilyn Sarkisian La Pierre is better known by what name?

22 Name the first "talkie", which appeared in 1927 and starred black-faced vaudeville artist Al Jolson.

23 Which Australian-born, Indian-raised actress said to have Asian blood married director Alexander Korda?

24 Who won the Miss Orange County beauty title and then appeared in films like *Grease 2* and *Scarface*?

25 Which champion swimmer starred in 1940s musicals featuring her spectacular underwater routines?

26 Who was the 1920s silent star who made a comeback in *Sunset Boulevard* as silent star Norma Desmond?

27 Which actor made famous by a film and TV sci-fi series called his autobiography *I Am Not Spock*?

28 Name the French pioneer who introduced the first newsreels in the early years of the century.

29 Which Italian director with an artistic first name is best remembered for his 1966 movie *Blow-Up*?

30 Which demanding actor, star of *48 Hrs* and *Q&A*, was once convicted of selling counterfeit draft cards?

HE'S NEVER HEARD OF ESSEX GIRLS.

Answers on page 223

Knowall's question:

Which great English composer wrote the *Enigma Variations?*

DELIUS !!!

1 What is the name of the highest female voice?

2 From which oratorio by Handel is the *Hallelujah Chorus?*

3 To which instrument does an orchestra usually tune?

4 Who composed *An American in Paris?*

5 In which area of London is the Royal Opera House?

6 What are the tonic sol-fa syllables in the major scale?

7 *Here Comes the Bride* is from which Wagner opera?

8 What is the meaning of *adagio* in terms of tempo?

9 What nationality was the composer Béla Bartók?

10 Which Austrian family is famous for composing waltzes?

11 In which London concert hall are The Proms held?

12 Julian Bream and John Williams play which instrument?

13 What is the name for a melody or tune for solo voice?

14 In which city is the largest opera house in the world?

15 Who was considered the greatest of violin-makers?

16 What term is used to denote "extremely quiet"?

17 Which is London's oldest orchestra still performing?

18 What is the name for a small concert piano?

19 Spanish composer Rodrigo suffers from what handicap?

20 Which northern orchestra moved to a new hall in 1996?

21 What is a song or hymn based on a biblical text?

WE LIVE IN HOPE.

22 What name is given to instruments such as the triangle?

23 Which city is home to Opera North?

24 Who were "The Mighty Handful"?

25 What are the names of "The Three Tenors"?

26 What is a Welsh festival of music and literature called?

27 In the 1750s, what was the "War of the Bouffons" about?

28 Which Russian composer died of cholera in 1893?

29 Who composed the Brandenburg Concertos?

30 Which popular work by Vivaldi divides up the year?

Answers on page 223

Knowall's question:

Which cycle of four operas by Wagner was first performed in 1876?

GÖTTERDÄMMERUNG ???

1 What is the name of the well-known tune for piano that can be played with one finger of each hand?

2 What is the name of the piece of carved wood that separates the strings of an instrument such as the cello?

3 Which German composer, whose works included nine popular symphonies, became increasingly deaf?

4 On which traditional collection of eastern tales is Rimsky-Korsakov's *Scheherezade* based?

5 *The Dance of the Sugar-Plum Fairy* is part of which ballet by Tchaikovsky?

6 What was the name of Daniel Barenboim's brilliant cellist wife who died of multiple sclerosis in 1973?

7 How long would you need to watch Wagner's opera *Siegfried* (including intervals), to the nearest 15 minutes?

8 Which American-born child prodigy violinist founded a school for talented young musicians in 1963?

9 Which piano suite by Mussorgsky was inspired by sketches and watercolours by Victor Hartmann?

10 What word indicates to string players that they should pluck rather than bow their strings?

11 The productions of which Russian impresario were designed by artists such as Picasso and Cocteau?

12 Which composer invented an imaginary Monsieur Croche as a mouthpiece for his own critical views?

13 Which satirical suite by Saint-Saëns depicts a swan, tortoises, fossils and pianists?

14 Which English "queen ballerina" was regularly partnered by Rudolf Nureyev?

15 Which opera by Verdi is a love story between the Egyptian commander Radames and a slave girl?

16 What is Prokofiev's "tale for children" in which each character is represented by a different instrument?

17 Which great American-born Greek diva had a close relationship with Aristotle Onassis?

18 Which brilliant 18th-century Austrian gave recitals aged six, composed his first opera aged 12 and died a pauper?

19 What is the name of the device used to muffle or modify the sound of a wind or string instrument?

20 In which orchestral suite does each movement represent a different heavenly body, and who wrote it?

21 Which American bandmaster and composer is known as "The March King"?

22 Which ballet by Delibes is based on a story by Hoffman about a toymaker who creates life-like dolls?

23 What name is given to music composed between about 1600 and 1750?

24 *Thus Spake Zarathustra* by Richard Strauss was popularised by which epic Stanley Kubrik film?

25 Which Russian chemist produced his opera *Prince Igor* in his spare time?

26 Which English conductor, famous for his wit, founded three orchestras and an opera company?

27 Which scenic cantata by Carl Orff is based on 13th-century poems about love, drink and other pleasures?

28 With which annual festival was the composer Benjamin Britten closely associated?

29 Which central London theatre is home to the English National Opera?

30 Which English composer, who died in 1958, was particularly influenced by indigenous folk songs?

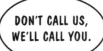

DON'T CALL US, WE'LL CALL YOU.

Answers on page 224

Knowall's question:

By what name is Schubert's Piano Quintet in A better known?

THE UNFINISHED !!!

1 Tchiakovsky was the subject of which Ken Russell film?

2 What is the Rossini opera *La Gazza Ladra* in English?

3 Which orchestral instrument has seven pedals?

4 What links Dvořák, Gorecki and Smetana?

5 Which German town hosts the annual Wagner festival?

6 Mozart's *Magic Flute* is set in which country?

7 Which French composer wrote *Symphonie Fantastique*?

8 Name three of the four types of saxophone.

9 Who wrote *The Young Person's Guide to the Orchestra*?

10 Which German composer died of syphilis at 31?

11 How many keys does a standard piano keyboard have?

12 Which popular opera features *The Toreador's Song*?

13 What musical term is literally "a joke" in Italian?

14 *Fidelio* was the only opera by which prolific composer?

15 What number is Tchiakovsky's *Pathétique Symphony*?

16 Mendelssohn's *Wedding March*, often played after the ceremony, is the overture to which piece of music?

17 What is the name for a composition featuring a solo instrument in combination with an orchestra?

18 In Classic FM's 1996 poll which resulted in their "Hall of Fame", which composer came out No. 1?

19 Which conductor began by being called from his cellist's chair to conduct *Aida* at Rio de Janeiro in 1886?

20 Who were the largest and most prolific composing family: Bach, Gershwin, Schumann, Strauss?

21 Which is the odd opera out: *La Bohème, Madame Butterfly, Tosca, La Traviata, Turandot*?

22 The prestigious Carl Flesch award is given for playing which instrument: violin, cello, piano or oboe?

23 Which piece of 17th-century music, originally attributed to Henry Purcell, is now credited to Jeremiah Clarke?

24 "Watch out for this young man. He is going to cause a stir in the world." Mozart talking about whom?

25 In 1775 Beaumarchais wrote the play on which one of Rossini's best-loved operas is based. Which one?

26 What are the four instruments that comprise the basic brass section of an orchestra?

27 Name one of the three operas by Giuseppe Verdi based on plays by Shakespeare.

28 Which Polish-born pianist, who died in 1982, enjoyed a concert career spanning 75 years?

29 French organist Oliver Messiaen's works were driven by mysticism and often included what natural sound?

30 Beethoven's *Eroica* Symphony (Third) was originally dedicated to which military leader and politician?

SOUNDS A BIT FISHY TO ME.

Answers on page 224

Knowall's question:

Who is the lead singer of Pulp?

JOE COCKER !!!

1 What band sold most albums in the UK in 1995?

2 How many No. 1 UK singles did The Who have?

3 What country do Ace of Base come from?

4 What was Spandau Ballet's only No. 1, In 1987?

5 What are the surnames of Robson and Jerome?

6 Which two big acts featured Jimmy Somerville?

7 Annie Lennox and Dave Stewart comprised who?

8 On which label do Blur record?

9 What nationality is the saxophonist Candy Dulfer?

10 Marc Almond was the vocalist with which group?

11 Who is the lead female singer of Portishead?

12 Name one of the Monkees – other than Davy Jones.

13 Who scored 10 with Sally, Lucille and Molly?

14 In what year was the Live Aid concert?

15 Why is Mark Chapman infamous in music history?

16 Who shared John Travolta's two No. 1 hits in 1978?

17 Who had *No Particular Place To Go* in 1964?

18 What was Scaffold's colourful No. 1 in 1968?

19 Which singer was in the Jam and the Style Council?

20 What was Neil Young's only No. 1 UK album?

21 Who is known as "the Godfather of Soul"?

22 What was the Beatles' last No. 1 hit in the UK?

23 In 1964, where was *The House of the Rising Sun*?

24 Name one of David Bowie's five No. 1 UK singles.

25 Who, along with Vince Clark, formed the duo Yazoo?

26 Which group evolved out of Joy Division?

27 What was the Beach Boys first UK No. 1 hit, in 1966?

28 Of which group was Simon Le Bon a member?

29 What Scottish group had two huge No. 1s in 1975?

30 Who was George Michael's partner in Wham!?

NO RELATION!

Answers on page 224

QUIZ NUMBER 80

Knowall's question:

What influential ITV pop show was hosted by Keith Fordyce and Cathy McGowan?

TOP OF THE POPS !!!

1 Gary Numan's well-known song *Cars* was used to advertise which company's lager in 1996?

2 Whose first two albums, identically titled but with different songs, both reached No. 1 in the UK?

3 Which female opera star sang the 1992 Olympic anthem *Barcelona* with Freddie Mercury of Queen?

4 The first to sell a million copies of a CD were Dire Straits. With which album?

5 What film soundtrack by Hazel O'Connor made No. 5 in the UK album charts in 1980?

6 Name one of the two singers who died with Buddy Holly in the plane crash of 1959.

7 Which unstoppable sex machine had a UK hit with the album *Starry Eyed and Bollock Naked* in 1994?

8 Which legendary Irish performer began his musical career in the 1960s with Them?

9 What bulbous performer was at No. 1 in the British pop charts on Christmas Day 1993?

10 The Beatles have spent more weeks in the UK album charts (1,160) than any other group. Who's second?

11 Name two of the three great rock guitarists who played with the Yardbirds in the 1960s.

12 Which fruitful Irish group enjoyed most "weeks" in the UK album charts in 1995, with a total of 96?

13 What was the title of Bob Dylan's first successful album in the UK, entering the charts in May 1964?

14 Which album by Meatloaf spent a record 472 weeks on the UK charts?

15 Cilla Black had two successive No. 1s in 1964 with *Anyone Who Had a Heart* and what other single?

16 What strange place was "all too beautiful" for the Small Faces in 1967?

17 Which is the odd one out: Degrees, Pennies, Seasons, Tops?

18 Who left the Hollies and joined David Crosby and Stephen Stills?

19 Holly Johnson's 4th No. 1 came with Paul McCartney, the Christians and Gerry Marsden. What was it?

20 In terms of albums, who was the best-selling female artist in Britain in 1994?

21 Who was the first singer ever to sell one million copies of a record worldwide?

22 *The Piper at the Gates of Dawn* was which rock group's debut album, in 1967?

23 The best-selling album in the US in 1995, with 11 million copies, was *Cracked Rear View*. By whom?

24 Who performed the female talking part on Mike Sarne's No. 1 hit *Come Outside* in 1962?

25 Which band made No. 1 in the UK charts with their first album, *I Should Coco*, in 1995?

26 Scouse comedian Alexei Sayle had a top 20 hit with what mickey-taking song in 1984?

27 In 1995 which female artist became the most successful French-Canadian act of all time?

28 Which album by Simon and Garfunkel spent 17 weeks at the top of the UK charts in 1971?

29 In the summer of 1996 Patsy Kensit became engaged to which leading music performer?

30 Only two acts have had three albums in the charts the same year: the Beatles (1965) and who else?

I'M READY TO GO FOR IT.

Answers on page 224

QUIZ NUMBER 81

Knowall's question:

Which pianist-singer is known as "The Genius"?

ELTON JOHN !!!

1 What instrument did Bix Beiderbecke play?

2 *One O'Clock Jump* was the theme tune of which band?

3 Who recorded *Jazz/Samba* with Charlie Byrd?

4 Which legendary singer's guitar was called "Lucille"?

5 What were Dizzy Gillespie's real first names?

6 The Modern Jazz Quartet comprise what instruments?

7 Who wrote Dave Brubeck's a massive hit *Take Five*?

8 What nationality was jazz guitarist Django Reinhardt?

9 Ludwik Zamenhov were the first names of which great?

10 Who had a 1961 hit with *Midnight in Moscow*?

11 Who is generally regarded as jazz's greatest bassist?

12 What two instruments gave Glenn Miller his "sound"?

13 Which jazz singer started out with Lionel Hampton?

14 Name the jazz violinist partner of Django Reinhardt.

15 Which writer described the 1920s as "The Jazz Age"?

16 Which trumpeter and bandleader has for years been chairman of BBC radio's *I'm Sorry I Haven't a Clue*?

17 Born Ferdinand Joseph La Menthe, he recorded in the 1920s with the Red Hot Peppers. Who was he?

18 Which jazzman commissioned George Gershwin to write *Rhapsody in Blue* – and first conducted it?

19 Name one of the two bands formed by English saxophonist Courtney Pine.

20 Who was the near-blind performer who became "the greatest pianist of all time", renowned for his technique?

21 Whose gravelly voice featured on songs such as *Got My Mojo Working* and *Hoochie-Coochie Man*?

22 The Chick Webb Band launched the career of which legendary female jazz singer, who died in 1996?

23 Which Harlem-based pianist and composer was known as "The Prophet" and "The High Priest of Bebop"?

24 Once with Benny Goodman, he was largely responsible for making the drums a solo instrument. Who is he?

25 Which U2 single, off *Rattle and Hum*, introduced BB King to a wider audience in 1992?

26 Which trumpeter won the Grammy Awards for both best classical soloist and best jazz soloist in 1984?

27 This sax player's ideas formed the basis of bebop and he teamed up with Dizzy Gillespie. Who was he?

28 Which blues great, born in 1917, has become known for recording with big names from the rock world?

29 Which American saxophonist is credited with making the baritone sax a successful solo instrument?

30 Who, according to legend, made a pact with the Devil for his haunting voice and guitar skills and died at 27?

Answers on page 225

QUIZ NUMBER 82

Knowall's question:

Which great songwriter was born in Peru?

PADDINGTON BEAR !!!

1. In 1961, who composed the music for *West Side Story*?

2. *People* and *Second-Hand Rose* come from which show?

3. Catfish Row is the setting for which Gershwin musical?

4. *Evita* was based on the life of which dictator's wife?

5. What was Elvis Presley's first movie, in 1957?

6. Which musical featured the song *Happy Talk*?

7. Name the two stars of *The King and I* on film?

8. What were George and Ira Gershwin's real first names?

9. *My Favourite Things* came from which 1960s musical?

10. For which British director was *Fame* a Hollywood debut?

11. Which actor sang *Bare Necessities* in *The Jungle Book*?

12. *John, Paul, George, Ringo and ...* who else?

13. *Cats* was based on a book by which American poet?

14. What links *Top Hat*, *Swing Time* and *Shall We Dance*?

15. In 1957, who played the lead role in *The Joker is Wild* ?

16 Who replaced Lorenz Hart as Oscar Hammerstein's lyricist to produce *Oklahoma!* in 1943?

17 *Pinball Wizard, I'm Free* and *See Me, Feel Me* came from which rock musical by The Who, filmed in 1975?

18 Which actor received rave reviews for his portrayal of Fagin in the 1967 film of Lionel Bart's *Oliver!*?

19 Who wrote the lyrics for *Moon River, That Old Black Magic* and *Jeepers Creepers*?

20 Which songwriting team had hits with *Brigadoon, Paint Your Wagon, My Fair Lady, Gigi* and *Camelot*?

21 The film version of which 1955 Broadway hit was released in the UK with the title *What Lola Wants*?

22 Which black bass singer made his name on stage with *Show Boat* in 1928, featuring *Ol' Man River*?

23 Who wrote the lyrics for *West Side Story* and both words and music for *A Little Night Music* in 1973?

24 Which 1954 MGM musical starring Howard Keel and Jane Powell has the same number twice in its title?

25 What unlikely book written by Victor Hugo in 1862 was turned into an international musical hit?

26 Which brothers wrote the music and lyrics for the songs in *Mary Poppins* and *The Jungle Book*?

27 *South Pacific* was on Broadway in 1949, but when did the film appear: 1950, 1952, 1954, 1956, 1958?

28 Gary Bond, Paul Jones, Jess Conrad, Jason Donovan, Phillip Schofield and Donny Osmond all played who?

29 Harold Arlen and E.Y. "Yip" Harburg wrote *Over the Rainbow,* sung by Judy Garland in which 1939 film?

30 Which English singer played Marilyn Monroe's boyfriend in *Let's Make Love* (1961)?

IT'S LIKE CARRYING COALS TO NEWCASTLE?

Answers on page 225

QUIZ NUMBER 83

Knowall's question:

What "dance" began in 1870 among the Paiute tribe and promised deliverance from the Indians' plight at the hands of the white man?

THE CONGA !!!

1 What kind of dancer was "Mr Bojangles"?

2 Prince Siegfried is the hero of which ballet?

3 Hamilton House and Petronella are kinds of what?

4 What dance move took Little Eva to No. 2 in 1962?

5 How many dancers feature in a *pas de deux*?

6 What do flamenco dancers hold in their hands?

7 The Royal Ballet is resident at which opera house?

8 How many beats in a bar does a waltz have?

9 *Dancing Queen* was a No. 1 hit for whom in 1976?

10 Name two of the ballets composed by Tchiakovsky.

11 What "dance troupe" was founded by Margaret Kelly?

12 In ballet, *jeté* is a type of what?

13 Which dancer is famous for "singin' in the rain"?

14 What dance was named after a street in London SE11?

15 The Princess of Wales is chief patron of which ballet?

16 Who "bumped" their way to No. 3 in 1974 and did very nicely with *Fancy Pants* the following year?

17 The Russian impresario Sergei Diaghilev founded which famous ballet company in Paris in 1908?

18 Which couple reunited in 1949 in *The Berkeleys of Broadway* after nine musical hits in the 1930s?

19 Who wrote the music for the ballet *Les Sylphides*: Berlioz, Chopin, Debussy, Ravel, Tchaikovsky?

20 The Charleston, *the* dance craze of the 1920s, originated in which southern American state?

21 What colour are the ballet shoes that couldn't stop dancing in the story by Hans Christian Andersen?

22 Which rounded performer's three dance-based hits came in 1961, 1975 and 1988?

23 Which prima ballerina with Sadler's Wells was later artistic director of the London Festival Ballet?

24 Which English composer had a hit in the West End and on Broadway with *Song and Dance*?

25 Margaret Hookham was the original name of which famous British prima ballerina?

26 *Dance On!* was an instrumental No. 1 for a group in 1962 and a female vocal No. 1 in 1963. Name one.

27 What nationality was dancer-choreographer Robert Helpmann: American, Australian, Austrian, German?

28 Born at Irkutsk, Siberia in 1938, defected to the West in 1961, died of Aids in 1993. Who was he?

29 Which French-sounding ballerina's 1957 autobiography was entitled *Come Dance With Me*?

30 Which traditional dance took The Brighouse and Rastrick Brass Band to No. 2 in the charts in 1977?

AT LEAST HE ENTERS INTO THE SPIRIT OF THINGS.

Answers on page 225

Knowall's question:

Which record company shrewdly decided that The Beatles weren't worth signing?

POLYGRAM !!!

1 An aircraft's "black box" flight recorder is called after which grasping king?

2 Which letter of the alphabet is represented in Morse Code by three dots?

3 How many red balls are on the table at the start of a snooker game?

4 Name the Roman Emperor who was ruling when the invasion of Britain began in 43AD.

5 What were all Britons able to enjoy for the first time on 29 May 1871?

6 At what point does water freeze on the Fahrenheit and Centigrade scales respectively?

7 How many states are there in the United Arab Emirates: three, five, seven, nine, eleven?

8 What was the name of the first spacecraft that actually landed on the Moon?

9 Which famous British professional sportsman won his first race in 1948 and his last in 1994?

10 What US Cavalry regiment did General Custer lead to disaster at Little Big Horn?

11 Which beleaguered City of London trading institution's hopeful motto is "In Utmost Good Faith"?

12 Which scale used to measure the velocity of wind is graduated from 0 to 12?

13 What piece of equipment used in women's field sports weighs 600g (21oz)?

14 American serial killer David Berkowitz was given what nickname by the media?

15 Who wrote in her diary: "I shall do my utmost to fulfil my duty towards my country. I am very young."?

16 How long does each quarter last in Australian Rules Football: 15, 20, 25, 30 or 35 minutes?

17 What animal was most used in Britain to do heavy farm work in the Middle Ages?

18 What building did British troops burn down on 24 August 1814?

19 How many known children did playwright William Shakespeare have?

20 What do banon, mimolette, monteray jack and samosoe have in common?

21 Which European nation was the first to defeat England at soccer in Britain?

22 What early fever remedy was extracted from the bark of the cinchona tree?

23 Who won the Miss Hungary beauty title in 1936 but had to give it up because she was under 16?

24 In 1977, which famous French film director played a scientist in *Close Encounters of the Third Kind*?

25 What sporting obstacle is three feet (91cm) high at its centre point?

26 Which caring organisation was established in Britain by Chad Varah in 1953?

27 Who was finally given the full rank and privileges of a British prince in 1957?

28 What team did Tranmere Rovers beat 13–4 in the highest-ever scoring game in English League football?

29 George V made the first royal Christmas broadcast in: 1924, 1928, 1932, 1936, 1940?

30 Which bird once common in Britain at locations like Salisbury Plain is the heaviest of all flying birds?

HE MIGHT GIVE THAT A SECOND LOOK.

Answers on page 225

Knowall's question:

What's the motor sport where monster vehicles aim to be fastest over very short distances?

WHEELIE RACING !!!

1 How did Charlotte Brew achieve a sporting first?

2 In which ancient country did polo originate?

3 Beckett's is on which famous motor-racing circuit?

4 How did the America's Cup get its name?

5 What was the triple jump originally called?

6 Who has scored the most runs in Test cricket?

7 Which country won the women's football in Atlanta?

8 On what surface is curling played?

9 How many people are allowed in a tug-of-war team?

10 What colour jacket is worn by US Masters winners?

11 Where do Ireland play home rugby union matches?

12 By what name is Rocco Marchegiano better known?

13 In which year did London last host the Olympics?

14 Who was John Newcombe's left-handed partner?

15 Sergei Bubka was top in what event for over a decade?

16 Who was the first cricketer to play in 100 Tests?

17 Which horse gave Willie Carson his first Derby win?

18 What two British football clubs are called the "Dons"?

19 Finn, Soling and Star are classes in which sport?

20 Which American golfer is known as "The Walrus"?

21 What is the lightest division in Olympic boxing?

22 At which Test venue could you watch from "The Hill"?

23 Captain Matthew Webb achieved what "first" in 1875?

24 Where is the All-England Lawn Tennis Club based?

25 Who set six athletics world records in an *hour* in 1935?

26 What is the nickname of S. Africa's rugby union team?

27 Name boxing's first black world heavyweight champion.

28 In which Scandinavian capital is the Bislett Stadium?

29 What is the usual diameter of a golf hole?

30 Whose record first-class cricket score did Brian Lara beat?

THIS GUY'S A REAL DRAG.

Answers on page 226

Knowall's question:

What comes next: double bogie, bogie, par, birdie, eagle, ... ?

VULTURE !!!

1 Which team reached the Super Bowl in three consecutive years (1991–93) and lost them all?

2 In which sport did Irina Rodnina win 23 World, Olympic and European gold medals?

3 Who is the odd man out: Agassi, Becker, Borg, Cash, Edberg, Krajeck, McEnroe, Sampras, Stich?

4 The 20th of 22 children, unable to walk until 11, she won three sprint golds in the Rome Olympics. Who?

5 Name one of the two Americans who have won the Formula 1 World Drivers' Championship.

6 Which Scottish golfer topped the European order of merit in 1993, 1994 and 1995?

7 Who was the first man to defeat Frank Bruno in his professional boxing career?

8 Kapil Dev holds the world record for Test match wickets: with 404, 414, 424, 434 or 444?

9 Which famous Australian rugby union try-scorer has spent most of his winters turning out in Italy?

10 Who lost an apparently unassailable lead to Nick Faldo in the last round of the 1996 US Masters?

11 Kent's 1950s wicket-keeper Godfrey Evans holds an unenviable negative Test batting record. What is it?

12 Where did Spain finish in the final medals table at the 1992 Olympics in Barcelona: 3rd, 6th, 9th, 12th?

13 Which country won the world national speedway championship in Germany in 1996?

14 Johnson was disqualified, Lewis moved up to gold and Christie was awarded silver. Who took bronze?

15 In which sport are knuckle balls, curved balls, screwballs and sliders delivered?

16 Dressage, cross-country and show-jumping are the elements of which equestrian sport?

17 What's missing: 100m, long jump, shot, high jump, 400m; 110m hurdles, discus, pole vault, javelin ..... ?

18 Mark Spitz won seven Olympic swimming gold medals in 1972. How many world records did he break?

19 Which Wigan player joined League's London Broncos and Union's Bedford in 1996?

20 Name the two players who scored 99 in the England-Australia Test at Lord's in 1993.

21 Who, having won the 1,500m in 1968, took the 3,000m steeplechase gold in 1972 for Kenya?

22 Whose record of 20 Wimbledon titles was Martina Navratilova chasing in her 1996 doubles matches?

23 Which two North-East clubs did Brian Clough, later more famous as a manager, play for?

24 Which England captain is the odd one out: Cowdrey, Dexter, Lewis, Denness, Brearley, Greig?

25 Why was Armin Hary's victory in the 1960 Olympic 100 metres in Rome thought to be suspect?

26 The modern pentathlon comprises swimming, running, riding, fencing and which other sport?

27 What game is played by the Pittsburgh Steelers, the San Francisco 49ers and the Washington Redskins?

28 What was unusual about the Irishman Eamonn Coughlan's sub four-minute mile in 1995?

29 How many players are there in an Australian Rules Football team: 12, 14, 16, 18, 20, 22?

30 In what year did Muhammad Ali (then Cassius Clay) win the Olympic light-heavyweight gold medal?

HIS MIND WANDERS SOMETIMES.

Answers on page 226

Knowall's question:

What parted company with Piquet, Prost, Mansell and Hill?

THE TRACK !!!

1 Which bowler has taken most World Cup wickets?

2 Tattenham Corner is on which famous racecourse?

3 Which great black US tennis player died of Aids?

4 What do the initials IAAF stand for?

5 Which woman golfer was rated world No. 1 in 1996?

6 Gunther Parche put which tennis player out of action?

7 Who first broke 13 sec. for the 100 metres hurdles?

8 Which New Zealander won six world speedway titles?

9 Where is the Grand Challenge Cup the oldest event?

10 Whose 1935 world long jump record lasted 25 years?

11 Bisley is Britain's premier venue for which sport?

12 Who won Wimbledon's first men's open singles title?

13 In 1993, who won the UK snooker title at 17?

14 Who is supposed to have "invented" rugby?

15 How many players are there in a volleyball team?

16 Which Welshman led the British Lions to their only Test series win over the All Blacks in 1973?

17 Who has scored most runs in first-class cricket: Geoff Boycott, W.G. Grace, Jack Hobbs or Wally Hammond?

18 Who was the first heavyweight to regain the world title when he beat Ingemar Johansson in 1960?

19 In 1996, which club beat St Helens to take the Stones Bitter Championship and avoid a trophy-less year?

20 In September 1996, which "plastic" company pledged £6 million to help "every level" of British sport?

21 Which Englishman took a record 4,187 first-class wickets at 16.71 apiece between 1898 and 1930?

22 Which Scotsman was world Grand Prix motor-racing champion in 1969, 1971 and 1973?

23 Who did Tim Henman beat in the 1996 US Open to avenge his earlier quarter-final Wimbledon defeat?

24 Which countryman replaced Pakistan's Jahangir Khan as the world's top squash player?

25 Which 'keeper holds the record for Test dismissals: Dujon, Evans, Grout, Healy, Knott, Marsh, Murray?

26 In which sport would you find the American star Fred Couples?

27 In 1986, which American cyclist became the first non-European to win the Tour de France?

28 Apart from Englishmen, who has been the most prolific scorer of runs in first-class cricket?

29 Which two players retained their US Open tennis singles titles at Flushing Meadow in 1996?

30 In August 1996, which son of a famous cricket father took five wickets on his first bowl for Hampshire?

FRANKLY, HE'S DERANGED.

Answers on page 226

Knowall's question:

Which pop singer played football for Real Madrid?

DIEGO MADONNA !!!

1 Who was the leading scorer in the 1986 World Cup?

2 What do the initials UEFA stand for?

3 Who moved across from Liverpool to Everton in 1992?

4 Why do Moscow Dynamo play in blue and white?

5 For what club did Ian Botham play professionally?

6 Who was the first professional player to be knighted?

7 Where did Juventus win the European Cup in 1996?

8 Who were League champions in 1971 and 1975?

9 Which Division 4 club reached the League Cup final?

10 Name the four clubs managed by Graham Taylor.

11 What links Chelsea, Milan, Spurs and West Ham?

12 Which club scored most League goals in 1995-96?

13 Who is the youngest Briton to be capped at full level?

14 Who put Newcastle out of the UEFA Cup in 1994-95?

15 Which League club was first to lay down artificial turf?

16 Against whom did Peter Schmeichel score in Europe?

17 Who took a dive at Hillsborough in August 1994?

18 In 1996, which Scottish club did Chris Waddle join?

19 What club won the first Football League title in 1889?

20 Who led the list of scorers in Euro '96?

21 Name the three Football League clubs called "Athletic".

22 Who moved from Porto to manage Barcelona in 1996?

23 What ground holds the world attendance record?

24 Rangers' 1996 League title took their run to how many?

25 Which British club was first to win a European trophy?

26 Who went from Istanbul to Southampton in 1996?

27 Which club won the European Super Cup in 1991?

28 Who did George Graham replace at Leeds United?

29 Who scored Arsenal's winner in 1979's FA Cup final?

30 What is the League title's biggest winning margin?

YOU HAVE TO BEGIN AT THE BEGUINING.

Answers on page 227

Knowall's question:

Why was it unlucky to be voted Footballer of the Year between 1985 and 1988?

THEY ALL BROKE A LEG !!!

1 Who's missing: Ball, Banks, J. Charlton, R. Charlton, Cohen, Hurst, Moore, Peters, Stiles, Wilson?

2 Discounting Bruce Rioch at Arsenal, who was the first major managerial casualty of 1996-97?

3 Which club went up and down all four divisions of the Football League in just nine seasons?

4 In 1996, what fact linked Benfica, Celtic, Juventus, Newcastle United, PSV Eindhoven and Valencia?

5 Name one of the two English players signed from Aston Villa by Bari for £800,000 in 1985.

6 What was special about Spurs' 2-1 victory over Forest at White Hart Lane on 2 October 1983?

7 Whose 1-0 win in Bulgaria enabled Ireland to reach the 1988 European Championship finals?

8 Who said in 1996: "I'm not finished with football, but football may be finished with me."?

9 Which two renowned "Rivs" played for Italy in the 1970 World Cup final against Rivelino's Brazil?

10 Who was lobbed by David Beckham and David Batty in his first two Premiership appearances of 1996-97?

11 Ray Wilkins was sent off playing for England in the 1986 World Cup finals. Against which country?

12 Which Northern Ireland club plays in the FAI League, the championship of the Republic?

13 Who is the odd man out: Francis, Gascoigne, Greaves, Hitchens, Hoddle, Ince, Law, Platt, Rush, Wilkins?

14 In 1985, which Manchester United player became the first player to be sent off in an FA Cup final?

15 Who, as a replacement for Pelé, scored for Brazil in the 1962 World Cup final against Czechoslovakia?

16 Which team beat Manchester United in the 1995 FA Cup final to foil their hopes of the "Double"?

17 Name the German who kept goal with a broken neck in the 1956 Cup final and was Footballer of the Year?

18 Which country won the Jules Rimet trophy outright at the 1970 World Cup finals?

19 Who is the only Briton to have twice been voted European Footballer of the Year by journalists?

20 The record attendance for a European Cup match is held by which British ground?

21 Which player, later Chelsea manager, scored 7 goals in 8 shots for Arsenal v Aston Villa in 1935?

22 Name one of the two players who scored for both sides in FA Cup finals in the 1980s.

23 Alfredo di Stefano, Real Madrid's great star of the 1950s, played for three countries. Can you name two?

24 Which Scot was sent home from the 1978 World Cup: Kenny Burns, Archie Gemmill or Willie Johnston?

25 How many goals did England concede in their six matches in the 1966 World Cup finals?

26 Johan Cruyff was succeeded as captain of Ajax and Holland by which defender?

27 How many goals did Just Fontaine score for France in the 1958 World Cup finals: 9, 10, 11, 12 or 13?

28 In 1971 Eddie Kelly became the first sub to score in an FA Cup final, but who originally claimed the goal?

29 Two countries have hosted the World Cup on two occasions. Name one of them – and the years.

30 Which Yorkshire club's stand drew widespread praise when it opened for business in 1995?

YOU ALWAYS WERE A LOSER.

Answers on page 227

Knowall's question:

Which car company made the revolutionary bike that took Chris Boardman to gold in the individual pursuit at Barcelona?

PEUGEOT !!!

1 Which Irish girl won three gold medals and a bronze in the pool at Atlanta in 1996?

2 Which of these colours is not used for a ring on the Olympic flag: green, yellow, blue, orange, black, red?

3 Who emulated Jesse Owens' 1936 performance by winning four track and field gold medals in 1984?

4 At Montreal in 1976, who became the first gymnast to record a perfect score of 10 in the Olympic Games?

5 Where did Britain finish in the overall 1996 medals table: 20th, 24th, 28th, 32nd, 36th, 40th?

6 Why were US 200-metre medallists Tommy Smith and Juan Carlos sent home from the 1968 games?

7 Which weightlifter who took gold at super-heavyweight in 1972 and 1976 later stood for president of Russia?

8 In which event in 1992 did a South African become the first black man to win a gold medal for his country?

9 Who shattered the world long jump record by 55cm (21.7in) in 1968, a mark that stood for 23 years?

10 Which aristocratic Frenchman was behind the revival of the modern Olympics at Athens in 1896?

11 When Sebastian Coe retained his 1,500 metres title at Los Angeles in 1984, who took the silver medal?

12 Why, since 1908, has the marathon been measured at exactly 26 miles and 385 yards?

13 Who banged his head on a board in 1988 but still managed to come up for a gold medal?

14 Paavo Nurmi won a record nine golds in distance athletics in the 1920s. What nationality was he?

15 Which US boxer managed only bronze in 1984 but later became heavyweight champion of the world?

16 What revolutionary high jump technique was introduced by the gold medallist at Mexico City in 1968?

17 Which film was based on the sprint rivalry between Harold Abrahams and Eric Liddell at Paris in 1924?

18 Which unlikely nation are the "reigning" Olympic rugby union champions?

19 Which New Zealander retained the 800 metres title in Tokyo in 1964 and also took gold in the 1,500?

20 Why did multi-gold medal gymnast Vera Cáslavská wear a black leotard at the Mexico games of 1968?

21 What nationality was mother-of-two Fanny Blankers-Koen, who won four athletics golds at London in 1948?

22 Who won three sprint golds in Seoul in 1988, complete with aerodynamic hood and flying fingernails?

23 Which amazing Czech athlete won the 5,000 metres, 10,000 metres and the marathon at Helsinki in 1952?

24 Name the three years in which the scheduled Olympics were "postponed" because of war.

25 Apart from Carl Lewis, who is the only athlete to win four successive gold medals in the same event?

26 When was tennis reintroduced into the Olympic Games: 1976, 1980, 1984, 1988 or 1992?

27 Who beat Jonathan Edwards into second place to take the triple jump gold medal at Atlanta in 1996?

28 Which Australian golden girl was sent home after a souvenir raid on the Japanese emperor's apartments?

29 Why was Italy's Dorando Pietri disqualified after winning the marathon in London in 1908?

30 What was unusual about the ancient Olympics from 720BC until they were discontinued centuries later?

THAT'S A TYPICAL FLOWERY ANSWER.

Answers on page 227

Knowall's question:

By what name was baseball star George Herman Ruth generally known?

GEORGIA PEACH !!!

1 Which US football franchise is affectionately known as "America's Team"?

2 Why will the name of James Naismith always have a place on the pages of American sporting history?

3 In which sport do teams compete annually for the coveted Stanley Cup?

4 How many points is a touchdown worth in the sport of American Football?

5 Which North American stadium hosted the final of the 1994 soccer World Cup?

6 Which US athlete was snubbed by Hitler at the 1936 Munich Olympics, and why?

7 With which celebrated team is basketball legend Michael Jordan associated?

8 Who was the first person to pitch a "perfect game" in baseball's World Series?

9 Which American Football team plays its home games in the Silverdome?

10 Which sport would you expect to see if you went to Flushing Meadow?

11 At which picturesque golf course is the US Masters traditionally held?

12 The film *Major League* follows the hilarious fortunes of which real-life baseball team?

13 What remarkable feat did basketball player Wilt "the Stilt" Chamberlain achieve in 1962?

14 Which New York Yankee married film star Marilyn Monroe in 1954?

15 What is the name of the ice hockey team owned by the Disney corporation?

16 Name one of the two Canadian teams playing baseball in the Major League in the mid-1990s.

17 Which American athlete won a record-equalling ninth Olympic gold at the 1996 Atlanta Games?

18 In what year was the first Superbowl held, and which team won?

19 Which famous basketball team was founded in Hinckley, Illinois by showman Abe Saperstein?

20 Who was the first American soccer player to be signed by an Italian league club?

21 Which baseball team won six consecutive World Series titles between the years 1949 and 1954?

22 With which predominantly American sport are Hulk Hogan and the British Bulldogs associated?

23 By what name is the premier motor racing series in the USA known?

24 What significant "first" did Jackie Robinson achieve in the game of baseball?

25 Who, followed by his own "army" of fans, was the first American golfing great of the modern era?

26 Two teams play professional ice hockey in New York. What are their names?

27 Which team set an unfortunate NFL record by losing four consecutive Superbowls between 1991 and 1994?

28 For which team did Pelé play in the inaugural American Soccer League?

29 Who is "The Fridge", and which English team did he leave America to join in 1996?

30 How many periods are there in an ice hockey match, and for how long does each one last?

Answers on page 228

Knowall's question:

What is the only weapon used by women in fencing?

THE ROLLING PIN !!!

1 How many counters does a backgammon player have?

2 In which sport would you see a "Sukahara"?

3 What is the maximum break possible in snooker?

4 Name one of the two schools at which fives originated?

5 How many players are there on a handball team?

6 Which letter, other than X, scores eight in *Scrabble*?

7 How many pieces are there in a set of dominoes?

8 What colour are goalkeepers' caps in water polo?

9 How many balls are used in billiards?

10 What hand is five cards of the same suit in poker?

11 The Swaythling Cup is a competition in which sport?

12 In charades, what does tugging your ear-lobe mean?

13 Wayne Gretzky is a prolific goalscorer – in what?

14 What two lifts constitute the total in weightlifting?

15 How many people play in a game of cribbage?

16 Six times World Open squash champion, he was undefeated from April 1982 to November 1986. Who?

17 In which county did the sport of badminton originate: Durham, Essex, Kent, Gloucestershire or Surrey?

18 On a British *Monopoly* board, what is the first property you reach after passing "Go"?

19 Who scored a perfect set of 6s for artistic interpretation in the 1984 ice skating pairs world championships?

20 Which Ipswich lad upset the form book to beat Eric Bristow in the final to take the 1983 world darts title?

21 Name the two Englishmen who have together won six world indoor bowls titles in the pairs?

22 Which card game played in casinos is also called vingt-et-un or 21?

23 Who won the 1985 world snooker final, watched by the largest post-midnight television audience ever?

24 Of which game was Egyptian film star Omar Sharif a master-player?

25 Match the sport to the lowest winning score in a game: badminton, squash, table tennis – 9, 21, 15.

26 In chess, which piece always remains on the same coloured squares?

27 In which sport did Anton Geesink (Holland) break the Japanese monopoly of the men's world titles?

28 In backgammon, what is a victory achieved before the loser has got his men to his own "table" called?

29 Sonja Henie won ten consecutive world ice skating titles from 1927. What nationality was she?

30 Which two events in international gymnastics are common to men's and women's competition?

THWARTED AGAIN...

Answers on page 228

Knowall's question:

Who was Phil Redmond referring to when he said: "He's a well-balanced athlete. He's got a chip on each shoulder."?

DALEY THOMPSON !!!

1 Stefan Edberg was beaten by which player in the 1996 US Open – his last Grand Slam appearance?

2 Which British golfer, uniquely, won the British Open and the US Open in the same year?

3 Gertrude Ederle became the first woman swimmer to accomplish what feat in 1926?

4 How many English Classic wins were recorded by Lester Piggott: 21, 23, 25, 27 or 29?

5 Which controversial distance runner from South Africa performed in bare feet in the 1980s?

6 Who was the last Briton to win the British Open squash championship?

7 Odd man out: Jacques Anquetil, Louison Bobet, Eddy Merckx, Bernard Hinault, Miguel Indurain.

8 Who broke Muhammad Ali's jaw in 1973: George Foreman, Joe Frazier, Larry Holmes or Ken Norton?

9 Which athlete's world record for 800 metres, set at Rieta, Italy, in 1981 was still standing 15 years later?

10 What was remarkable about Monégasque Louis Chinon's victory in the 1955 Monaco Grand Prix?

11 Who was Britain's top scorer when they won the Olympic men's hockey gold medal at Seoul in 1988?

12 Which Australian made his second Wimbledon singles final appearance 20 years after his first?

13 Which British hurdler regularly beat Colin Jackson and Tony Jarrett over 110 metres as a junior?

14 Rudy Hartono (8) holds the record for most wins in the All-England Championships. In which sport?

15 Who broke the world cycling records for the 4,000m pursuit and the 1-hour at Manchester in 1996?

16 Why were the Italian crowd delighted when Michael Schumacher took the chequered flag at Monza in 1996?

17 Which darts player has recorded most wins in both the World Open Championship and the World Masters?

18 Who is the only woman to have won the prestigious London Marathon on three occasions?

19 Odd man out: Terry Griffiths, Joe Johnson, John Parrott, Dennis Taylor, Cliff Thorburn, Jimmy White.

20 Name one of the two men who have won all four skiing titles at one single world championship?

21 Who was the first jockey to win both the English Derby and the Kentucky Derby?

22 Why was the 1921 world heavyweight fight between Jack Dempsey and Georges Carpentier a milestone?

23 Which rugby union player became a TV sports quiz captain after leading England to a Grand Slam?

24 Who first broke 10 sec. for the 100m: Valeriy Borzov, Armin Hary, Bob Hayes, Carl Lewis, Jesse Owens?

25 Which Pakistani bowler passed 300 wickets in Tests playing against England at The Oval in 1996?

26 In 1985, who became the youngest men's singles champion in Wimbledon history at the age of 17?

27 Which boxer, the only world heavyweight champion to retire undefeated, died in a plane crash in 1969?

28 Which England rugby star was appointed director of coaching at Gosforth in 1995?

29 Who retired from Test cricket in 1995 after a record number of caps (118) and runs (8,900) for England?

30 Who did Henry Cooper beat to become British and Empire heavyweight boxing champion in 1959?

YOU'VE GOT LESS THAN 10 SECONDS TO ANSWER.

Answers on page 228

Knowall's question:

Who wrote the all-time classic cookery manual *Household Management?*

DELIA SMITH !!!

1 Caviar, regarded by many as the ultimate delicacy, is principally the salty roe of which fish?

2 The "Oyster" is a famous model produced by what top Swiss watchmaker?

3 What is "forever", and has also been described as "a girl's best friend"?

4 Name the two staple ingredients from which vodka can be distilled.

5 The Granny Smith is regarded as a classic "British apple", but in what country was it first developed?

6 What is the proper medical name for the illness sometimes called "Yuppie flu"?

7 Which jewellery chain store boss infamously remarked that his shops sold "crap"?

8 Name the designer of the "little black dress" whose real name was Gabrielle Bonheur.

9 From which region of France does the wine accurately called claret originate?

10 The fur of which animal was so valuable that for many years Russia refused to export breeding specimens?

11 What is the name of the foot-shaped form used by a traditional cobbler to make shoes?

12 In 1657, to whom was the first pineapple ever to arrive in Britain presented?

13 Will a *steak tartare* always be cooked as: rare, medium rare, well done?

14 What is the most important single ingredient of *pâté de foie gras*?

15 What new drink was perfected by cellarer Dom Pierre Perignon at the French abbey of Hautvillers in 1698?

16 What is the source of the wool used to make super-soft angora garments?

17 Name the loose-leaf personal organiser that became an essential tool of the upwardly mobile in the 1980s.

18 What hedgerow fruit is traditionally used to produce a red fortified gin?

19 In which century did tobacco smoking become a widespread habit in Europe?

20 What precious metal mined in tiny quantities is often deemed more desirable than gold?

21 Which rich meringue-based dessert item was named after a famous Russian ballerina?

22 For which fortified wines long popular in Britain are Spain and Portugal respectively known?

23 Who was the English fashion designer who made his name in the 1960s and was murdered in 1996.

24 Which dictator's wife is said to have amassed the world's largest-ever collection of shoes?

25 Commercial meat-farming of what exotic African species is becoming increasingly common in Britain?

26 A bottle of dessert wine from which French Château was sold for £5,000 in 1996?

27 What would appear in a French restaurant in response to an order for *escargots*?

28 "Mad cow disease" changed the eating habits of Europe. What is its scientific name?

29 What basic open-top version of the Mini-Minor became fashionable transport in 1960s London?

30 Which British prime minister had Pol Roger champagne specially bottled in imperial pint bottles?

THAT ONE'S HARD TO BEAT.

Answers on page 229

Knowall's question:

The flowers and berries of which tree are respectively used to make a cordial and full-bodied red country wine?

THE BLACKTHORN !!!

1 What fiery new spirit did the Spanish start producing from sugar-cane in Barbados around 1600?

2 Which American desert town legalised gambling in 1931 and now contains the legendary "Strip"?

3 Which herb is used in pesto sauce, providing its green colour: basil, mint, rosemary, sage, thyme?

4 In 1875 what food did Seventh Day Adventist John Kellogg invent, claiming it would help curb sex drive?

5 For the manufacture of what luxury item is the island of Cuba best known?

6 What store chain founded by Anita Roddick specialises in natural cosmetics and toiletries?

7 The making of what dessert item was perfected by Sicilian Francisco Procopio in 1659?

8 In what year was the Sony Walkman introduced: 1971, 1975, 1979, 1983 or 1987?

9 Which nut when ground forms the principal ingredient of marzipan?

10 What is the name of the massage treatment based on the use of essential oils?

11 With what natural food are Butley in Suffolk and Whitstable in Kent particularly identified?

12 What are the two principal ingredients of a "Bloody Mary" cocktail?

13 Name the simple furniture in the style of an American religious sect which became popular in the 1990s.

14 What did John Hawkins bring from America to England in 1564, which became an important staple food?

15 What were the 1950s followers of rock 'n' roll who wore thick crêpe-soled shoes and drape jackets called?

16 Which American manufacturer began the bottling and marketing of tomato ketchup in 1876?

17 What Class B drug illegally used for recreational purposes is sometimes known as "ganja"?

18 What "intellectual beverage and temperance drink" did John Pemberton introduce to America in 1886?

19 Apart from the heart, lungs and liver of a sheep or calf, what are the two main ingredients of haggis?

20 What is the 1990s term euphemistically used to described the sacking of company employees?

21 In what year was the first self-service restaurant in the USA opened: 1893, 1903, 1913, 1923 or 1933?

22 What wine is the subject of an annual race to get the first bottle from France to London?

23 Which successful English spy author first made his reputation as a cookery journalist and writer?

24 Jojoba is principally used in the manufacture of what type of products?

25 Beetroot is the main ingredient of what soup that originated in Eastern Europe?

26 Which British fashion designer is credited with popularising the mini-skirt in the 1960s?

27 What canned soup brand introduced in 1897 was later immortalised by American pop artist Andy Warhol?

28 From what staple ingredient is the Japanese alcoholic drink saki made?

29 In the 1960s, what trendy London boutique was opened by Barbara Hulanicki in Kensington?

30 By what name do Americans know the English City gent's bowler hat?

HE GETS OLDER BUT NO WISER.

Answers on page 229

QUIZ NUMBER 96

Knowall's question:

What hobby would involve throwing a pot?

GARDENING !!!

1 Who would refer to books by Leslie Halliwell?

2 What does a lepidopterist collect?

3 Which "Goodie" is also an avid "twitcher"?

4 What is the Japanese art of paper folding called?

5 What should you do in a Laser or a Mirror?

6 Who would use the Stanley Gibbons catalogue?

7 What is the lowest registered handicap in golf?

8 For what hobby do TSR cater?

9 What are British Blues and Turkish Vans?

10 Which cartoonist famously parodied the Pony Club?

11 What is the passion of an oenophile?

12 Chain, blanket and cross are types of what?

13 What runs from 16 June to 15 March?

14 In which sport is an E7.7b the greatest challenge?

15 With what do you associate "The Enigmatist"?

16 Who would use burnt sienna and cobalt blue?

17 What is the more common name for ikebana?

18 Which footpath runs from Edale to Kirk Yelholm?

19 In which room in the house would you find a wok?

20 What does "karate" mean in English?

21 What is Britain's rarest stamp?

22 From which religion does yoga originate?

23 What does the acronym CAMRA stand for?

24 Who would be pleased to see a Royal Scotsman?

25 What does base jumping involve?

26 To which craft do the weft and warp apply?

27 What are listed in the *Miller's Price Guide*?

28 How many people perform a Scottish sword dance?

29 Macramé is the art of making what?

30 How is a collector of coins officially described?

I THINK THE GLAZED EXPRESSION SAYS IT ALL.

Answers on page 229

Knowall's question:

After what character in Greek mythology was the garden bulb *amaryllidaceae* named?

DAPHNE !!!

1 Which garden plant provides the drug digitalis?

2 What can be cabbage, tea or moss?

3 Montana and Nelly Moser are what variety of plant?

4 Box or yew clipped into shapes is called what?

5 What herb is used to make the drink absinthe?

6 What's missing: "Never cast a clout till *what* is out."

7 What plant was originally known as the love apple?

8 Cara and King Edward are varieties of what?

9 In which country did tulips originate?

10 What is the flowering houseplant *Impatiens Walleriana*?

11 What are the green flies which suck sap and eat leaves?

12 What kind of soil do azaleas prefer?

13 Which garden plant is called ling in the wild?

14 A dibber is what kind of gardening tool?

15 What kind of fruit is a Worcester?

16 Deadly nightshade is related to which vegetable?

17 Who planted the famous white garden at Sissinghurst?

18 Which plant, other than grass, was used for lawns?

19 A plant produced by crossing varieties is called what?

20 What is used to make candied green cake decoration?

21 Chives are the cousin of which vegetable?

22 What is the popular name of the weed *Convolvulus*?

23 What is distinctive about an espaliered tree?

24 What do viticulturists cultivate?

25 Who marketed the most famous potting compost?

26 What plants can store water in their leaves or stems?

27 What does the adjective "hardy" mean to gardeners?

28 What is grown in a potager?

29 The botanist Leonhard Fuchs named which flower?

30 What is the name for Japanese miniature trees?

TAKE A LOOK IN THE MIRROR.

Answers on page 229

Knowall's question:

Whose original name was Mortimer Mouse?

JERRY !!!

1 When did Bill Bixby become Lou Ferrigno?

2 Conkers are the fruit of which tree?

3 What was home to the mice in *Bagpuss*?

4 Which lad from *The Biz* later starred in *EastEnders*?

5 In ballet, what does *plié* mean?

6 Who played Lex Luthor in the *Superman* movies?

7 What was Wendy's surname in J. M. Barrie's *Peter Pan*?

8 Brian Bolland created which fearsome comic character?

9 Who played the Sheriff of Nottingham in *Maid Marian*?

10 What was Walt Disney's first full-length animated movie?

11 Who is the father of Jackie's baby in *Roseanne*?

12 What did Old Mother Hubbard fetch from the cupboard?

13 Name the holiday camp featured in *Hi De Hi!*

14 Who is the aardvark in *Saturday Aardvark*?

15 What links *Grange Hill, Brookside* and *Hollyoaks*?

16 Where do George Trotter and Emma Brierly meet?

17 Which television show seeks Britain's best young cook?

18 Gallifrey is the home planet for which famous doctor?

19 Which woodwind instrument is the "highest"?

20 What nationality is Bjork?

21 What Chinese dish literally means " bits and pieces"?

22 The Owl and the Pussycat were married by who?

23 What kind of animal was Thomas O'Malley?

24 What Ancient Greek became famous for his fables?

25 Who wrote the music for, and starred in, *Labyrinth*?

26 What colour are the stripes in Wally's hat?

27 Celeste was married to what fictional French elephant?

28 Who played the female lead in the *Ghostbusters* films?

29 What was Grotbag's unusual method of transport?

30 In which television hospital does Charlie Fairhead work?

Answers on page 229

Knowall's question:

Who created the immortal Peter Rabbit and Jemima Puddleduck?

ENID BLYTON !!!

1 For what crime was Toad jailed in Kenneth Grahame's *The Wind in the Willows*?

2 Which hot female pop group became the darlings of the industry in the summer of 1996?

3 What was the queen eating when the blackbird pie was "opened"?

4 How did the Wicked Witch of the East die in L. Frank Baum's book *The Wizard of Oz*?

5 Which fictional vehicle was "bought" for just £50,000 in 1980 – and had made £1.2 billion by 1996?

6 Which super television character was played by Gudrun Ure in 1985?

7 How many muscles are there in an elephant's trunk: 4, 40, 400, 4,000, 40,000?

8 The hugely successful 1996 film *Babe* was based on the book *The Sheep-Pig*. Who wrote it?

9 Which foxy puppet's masters have included Rodney Bewes, Derek Fowlds and Roy North?

10 What two animals led Pinocchio astray as the wooden puppet made his way to school?

11 Luke McMasters is the real name of which huge television wrestling star?

12 In *Gulliver's Travels*, what caused the war between Lilliput and their neighbours?

13 What did the huntsman show to the queen to "prove" that he had killed Snow White in the woods?

14 In *Rub-a-dub-dub*, what were the occupations of the three men in the tub?

15 How do the dogs disguise themselves to escape from the evil Cruella de Vil in *101 Dalmatians*?

16 What are the names of the lion king and the evil lion in Disney's *The Lion King*?

17 What did Hansel hold out to the witch to convince her that it was his finger?

18 Which small group did a cover version of *I Want To Be a Hippy,* and what did they call their hit song?

19 In the song, how many men were under the command of The Grand Old Duke of York?

20 Which country produced Hans Christian Andersen, the best known of fairy story writers, and Lego?

21 In Roald Dahl's *The Twits*, what makes Mrs Twit think that she is getting shorter?

22 What was the name of Ariel's lobster friend in *The Little Mermaid?*

23 Spot the odd one out: Cobra, Hunter, Jet, Knight, Lightning, Warrior, Zodiac.

24 Why did the Pied Piper of Hamelin lead the children off into the mountains?

25 Which female character in *Home and Away* was in trouble with the immigration authorities in 1996?

26 Which of Charles Dickens' novels features many characters and events from his own life?

27 Colonel Mustard and Professor Plum are two of the male suspects in *Cluedo*. Who is the third?

28 A lovable witch, the "Draw People", "Hangle" and "Phoebe the Phone" all feature in which programme?

29 Who wrote the music for both *Toy Story* and *James and the Giant Peach*?

30 Who was the member of Take That who left the group in 1995 shortly before it broke up?

RABBITS DRIVE ME POTTY.

Answers on page 230

QUIZ NUMBER 100

Knowall's question:

On which Hebridean island is the town of Tobermory located?

SKYE !!!

1 How many times did James Bond star Sean Connery actually play 007?

2 What reflective road safety aid was invented by Percy Shaw in 1934?

3 Which European country occupied Casablanca during World War 2?

4 Which three West Ham United players were in England's 1966 World Cup-winning team?

5 What is the average life span of an African elephant: 25, 35, 40, 45 or 50 years?

6 Which continental car company first adopted its distinctive diamond-shaped badge in 1924?

7 What is the most southerly national capital city in the world at 41° south?

8 Which father-and-son team both won Oscars for *The Treasure of Sierra Madre* in 1948?

9 What word has been incorporated into over one thousand languages without changing?

10 What climbing orchid with fleshy leaves and fragrant greenish-white flowers is used as a flavouring?

11 In 1946, what method of dating ancient objects did American Willard Libby devise?

12 Where did the second modern Olympic Games take place in 1900?

13 Roughly what percentage of the population is left-handed: 4%, 9%, 14%, 19%, 24%?

14 Which accomplished British horseman was flat racing's champion jockey on 26 occasions?

15 What is the imaginative name of the new bridge linking England and Wales?

16 What collectively are Yale, Harvard, Columbia, Brown, Princeton, Pennsylvania, Cornell and Dartmouth?

17 Who was elected as the first president of the French Fifth Republic in 1958?

18 What lies between infra-red waves and radio waves in the electro-magnetic spectrum?

19 The highest recorded number of children born to a single British woman was: 34, 36, 38, 40, 42?

20 In golf, what common location is shared by all courses called "links"?

21 During the English Civil War, which general defeated Charles I at the battle of Naseby?

22 Through which sprawling city does the 48-kilometre (30-mile) Figueroa Street run?

23 What condiment is said to have been created in the 18th century by Durham woman Mrs Clements?

24 Up, down, top, bottom, strange, charm and Version 3.31 all have what in common?

25 Which significant "first" was achieved by Frank Harpo and George Samuelson in 1896?

26 What is curious about John Cage's musical piece *Four Minutes and Thirty-three Seconds*?

27 The lowest completed total in a one-day cricket international was 43, scored by which country in 1993?

28 Which of the Channel Islands covers an area of 116 square kilometres (45 square miles)?

29 How many films did Marilyn Monroe actually make: 14, 19, 24, 29, 34?

30 The maximum permitted length of what piece of sporting equipment is 97cm (38in)?

PERHAPS HE SHOULD THINK THAT OVER.

Answers on page 230

ANSWERS

Quiz 1

Knowall's answer: In the human pancreas

1. Coventry
2. Esperanto
3. Gargoyle
4. 1838
5. Assassins
6. Guy Fawkes
7. The Hippocratic Oath
8. Dry ice
9. Colonel (later Lord) Robert Baden-Powell
10. The Wailing Wall
11. The Grand National Steeplechase
12. Sherlock Holmes, Dr Watson, Mrs Hudson
13. The *Kon-Tiki* Expedition
14. Charlemagne
15. The American Civil War
16. 1852
17. William Booth
18. Fort Knox
19. The South Sea Bubble
20. Felix Wankel
21. Severn bore
22. Hereward the Wake
23. The safety match
24. The dome of St Paul's Cathedral
25. Klondike
26. World's largest painting at 410 by 70 feet (130 by 21 metres)
27. It's "Robinson Crusoe's" island
28. The five inhabited continents
29. Paul Revere
30. Ivan Lendl

Quiz 2

Knowall's answer: 150

1. 1 million
2. Ringo Starr
3. 39
4. Switzerland
5. No. 5
6. 101
7. A statute mile
8. 20th
9. 23 is the next prime number (a number that can be divided only by itself and 1)
10. Hydrogen
11. 16
12. 78
13. Perfect numbers (the sum of all their factors, e.g. 28 = 1+2+4+7+14)
14. 0 and 1
15. 500 years
16. 14 (it's always 14)
17. Bashful
18. The Third Republic
19. *The Seven Samurai* (warriors)
20. 10
21. 1471

22. A cable (a league is 3 nautical miles)
23. 666
24. They all died at that age
25. The murder of O. J. Simpson's wife Nicole and Ron Goldman
26. 65-70
27. The sale of alcoholic liquor ("Prohibition")
28. "Twenty thousand"
29. The internationally agreed definition of a second in time
30. Castlemaine

Quiz 3

Knowall's answer: 47

1. 24
2. 21.30
3. Australia and New Zealand (The Australian and New Zealand Army Corps)
4. Christmas Day
5. 12 August (the "Glorious Twelfth")
6. Greenwich Mean Time and British Summer Time
7. President John F. Kennedy
8. 23 April
9. March (Mars)
10. Traditionally, money from boxes placed in church during the Christmas services was distributed to the poor of the parish
11. 7am
12. Ante-meridian (Latin = before noon) and post-meridian (after noon)
13. Lace
14. 14 July
15. Shrove Tuesday
16. Marbles
17. 15th
18. A day
19. All Saints' Day
20. The solstices
21. 11 November (peace in 1918 was signed "on the 11th hour of the 11th day of the 11th month")
22. Thanksgiving Day
23. He reversed the year he wrote it – 1948
24. Empire Day
25. The 50th anniversary of VE-Day and VJ-Day
26. Jewish
27. The July Plot
28. 24 hours
29. 5
30. November

Quiz 4

Knowall's answer: A school of whales

1. Blitz
2. Cayman
3. Improvise
4. Friday, the day of Frig
5. A dish of raw fish
6. A jumbo
7. Oporto, Portugal
8. Using the telephone
9. A raspberry
10. *Fait accompli*
11. A herbaceous plant
12. A furlong – literally a "furrow long"
13. Parliament
14. A gourmet enjoys fine

food, a gourmand is
gluttonous
15. The chair
16. *Grand Prix*
17. "So long"
18. The Duke of Wellington
19. Late 1940s, early 1950s
(a period of exception-
ally high birth rate)
20. *Zeitgeist*
21. A pleasant or
wholesome appearance
22. Noodle
23. A yard
24. Oral, because it is
spoken (aural is heard)
25. A traditional spread of
food from Sweden
26. Lady Godiva
27. Kenny Everett
28. "e"
29. (Giovanni Jacopo)
Casanova
30. They are both a "galley"

Quiz 5

**Knowall's answer: To a
"sickening" extent**
1. The highest and lowest
tides
2. Young women used to
prepare for marriage in
the "spin-house"
3. Rank and file members
4. To feint is to pretend, to
faint is to swoon
5. Roman Latin
6. A duke or bishop
7. Energising
8. A pride
9. They are decisively
defeated
10. 111 and its multiples

11. Having a look
12. Slowly
13. Switzerland
14. At an American
university
15. Either of the day's two
short watches
16. Toledo
17. Reply (*Respondez s'il
vous plait*)
18. Because it is a small
blister
19. A male cow, female yak
20. Doppelgänger
21. A deck of cards
22. No choice at all
23. Buddhism
24. The funny bone
25. Alpha, beta, gamma
26. Football's first division
27. A thief
28. Apply the final or
decisive stroke
29. Open spaces
30. Fights bulls

Quiz 6

Knowall's answer: 13
1. Stealing
2. A petrol bomb
3. His name is the work's
title
4. A brutal Turkish
irregular soldier
5. A baby or toddler
6. Magnus Magnusson
7. Vulpine
8. The "old boy network"
9. A wasp
10. Birds' eggs
11. At the bottom of the
ocean
12. A son's sexual desire

for his mother
13. *Persona non grata*
14. A World War 1
long-range German gun
15. The Greek goddess of
victory
16. A leveret
17. The wife
18. Belladonna
19. Smallpox
20. A type of cloth
21. Traitors
22. Discrete – separate
existence; discreet –
circumspect
23. Hungary
24. Hogmanay
25. An indiscretion or
social slip
26. Termites
27. Taking pleasure in
others' misfortune
28. An old hunting cry
29. A sleuth
30. As an *annus horribilis*

Quiz 7

**Knowall's answer:
The police**
1. Vera Lynn
2. The Boeing 747

3. "The Sunshine State"
4. An inflatable lifejacket
5. The Duke of Wellington
6. A geyser in Yellowstone
Park
7. Erwin Rommel
8. *The Times*
9. Alex Higgins
10. The "Tommy" (from
"Tommy Atkins")
11. The United States flag
12. Lillie Langtry
13. "The Big Cat"
14. Bachelor PM Edward
Heath
15. The staid Bank of
England
16. The tiger
17. Rasputin
18. Ireland
19. "The Golden Girl"
20. George Stephenson's
first steam locomotive
(1814)
21. Louis Armstrong
22. The striking *bell* in
parliament's clock
tower
23. "Mother's ruin"
24. Florence Nightingale
25. An army fire engine
26. A "ship of the desert"
27. Oil
28. Frank Tyson
29. New York City
30. Greg Norman

Quiz 8

**Knowall's answer:
John Wayne**
1. Arthur Wellesley
2. They were both women
writing under a man's

ANSWERS

name (Mary Ann Evans, Amandine Dupont)
3. Cat Stevens
4. The Marquess of Queensberry
5. Saki
6. Lewis Carroll (*Alice in Wonderland*)
7. Charles Manson
8. Pablo Picasso
9. Bono and The Edge
10. Harold Robbins
11. Bonnie Prince Charlie
12. Virgil
13. Sugar Ray Robinson
14. George Orwell
15. Kiki Dee
16. Groucho, Harpo, Chico and Zeppo Marx
17. St Francis of Assisi
18. John Denver
19. Tom Thumb
20. Tintoretto
21. Stalin
22. Henry Root
23. Sundance
24. Kenny Everett
25. Lord Longford
26. Grandma Moses
27. Engelbert Humperdinck
28. Rock Hudson

29. Emma, Lady Hamilton
30. Ho Chi Minh

Quiz 9

Knowall's answer:
Oscar Wilde
1. Richard III in Shakespeare's play
2. Harold Wilson
3. Pablo Picasso
4. US astronaut Buzz Aldrin
5. Simone de Beauvoir
6. Captain Lawrence Oates
7. Marie Antoinette, wife of Louis XVI
8. Muhammad Ali (Cassius Clay)
9. Margaret Thatcher
10. Russian spy Kim Philby
11. Benjamin Franklin
12. Neville Chamberlain
13. Paul McCartney
14. Richard Nixon
15. Joseph P. Kennedy (JFK's father)
16. Rudyard Kipling
17. Movie mogul Sam Goldwyn
18. Napoleon Bonaparte
19. Queen Victoria
20. Goethe (last words)
21. Frank Bruno
22. Socrates
23. Mandy Rice-Davies
24. Emile Zola (on the Dreyfus case)
25. Lord Baden-Powell
26. Winston Churchill
27. Phineas T. Barnum
28. Labour leader Hugh Gaitskell
29. King George V (last

words)
30. Irish rebel Michael Collins

Quiz 10

Knowall's answer:
General Charles de Gaulle
1. Henry Stanley
2. Winston Churchill
3. Henry Kissinger
4. Adolf Hitler
5. George Orwell (in *1984*)
6. Painter J. M. W. Turner (last words)
7. President Harry Truman
8. Charles Atlas (Angelo Siciliano)
9. W. H. Auden (in the poem *September 1, 1939*)
10. Lenin
11. *Maigret* creator Georges Simenon (his wife reckoned nearer 2,000)
12. Noël Coward (on his deathbed)
13. Mao Tse-tung
14. Entertainer Liberace
15. President Lyndon B. Johnson
16. Composer Gustav Mahler (last word)
17. Henry Ford
18. Martin Luther King
19. *Manchester Guardian* editor C. P. Scott
20. PM Edward Heath
21. Charles II (on his deathbed)
22. President Franklin D. Roosevelt
23. W. C. Fields
24. John Lennon

25. First credited to Stokely Carmichael
26. Nicaraguan dictator Anastasio Somoza
27. John McEnroe
28. PM Harold Macmillan
29. Empire builder Cecil Rhodes (last words)
30. First credited to Al Jolson (in *The Jazz Singer*)

Quiz 11

Knowall's answer: Lady Caroline Lamb
1. Lord Lucan
2. Boris Yeltsin
3. Edith Cavell
4. Maxwell Communications Corporation
5. Freddie Mercury
6. Bill Clinton's
7. David Lloyd George
8. Julie Ward
9. Rupert Brooke
10. Michael Milken
11. Isadora Duncan's
12. Ayatollah Khomeni
13. England's
14. Smoking
15. Nelson Mandela's wife Winnie
16. Bernhard Langer's
17. Pancho Villa
18. Claus von Bulow's
19. First man to die in a passenger train accident
20. *Spycatcher*
21. Enrico Caruso
22. King Edward VII
23. Evelyn Waugh's
24. Princess Diana

25. *Mein Kampf* ("My struggle")
26. Leona Helmsley
27. An earthquake
28. Alan Bond
29. Sir Jock Delves Broughton
30. Erich Honecker

Quiz 12

Knowall's answer: Paddy Ashdown
1. Ronald Reagan
2. Archduke Franz Ferdinand of Austria-Hungary
3. Mikhail Gorbachev of the Soviet Union
4. Kurt Waldheim
5. Nigel Lawson
6. Fidel Castro
7. Muhammad Ali
8. Sylvio Berlusconi
9. Dylan Thomas
10. David Mellor
11. Raymond Illingworth
12. Roscoe "Fatty" Arbuckle
13. President John F. Kennedy
14. *This Is Your Life*
15. Archduke Rudolf
16. The SDP (Social Democratic Party)
17. Michael Jackson
18. Major Ronald Ferguson
19. George Bernard Shaw
20. John Maynard Keynes
21. Marc Bolan
22. Arthur Scargill
23. Matrix Churchill
24. Joan Baez
25. Idi Amin

26. The "Lavender List"
27. Lillie Langtry
28. The Archbishop of Canterbury's
29. John Poulson
30. He was hanged for spying

Quiz 13

Knowall's answer: Nicholas Ridley
1. John Selwyn Gummer
2. Emmeline Pankhurst
3. Prince Charles's
4. Lady Bienvenida Buck
5. Woodrow Wilson
6. Matt Busby
7. Brian Jones
8. Vidkun Quisling
9. Peter Rachman
10. Auguste Rodin
11. Ulrike Meinhof
12. Malcolm X
13. William Randolph Hearst
14. Carlos the Jackal (Ilyich Ramirez Sanchez)
15. Lester Piggott
16. The Marquess of Queensbury
17. Dr Marie Stopes
18. Ernest Saunders
19. By radio signal
20. Gough Whitlam
21. L. Ron Hubbard
22. William McKinley
23. Jeremy Thorpe
24. Diego Maradona
25. Leni Riefenstahl
26. Richard Strauss
27. Presidential hopeful Gary Hart
28. Anwar Sadat

29. Nadia Comaneci
30. The Christian Democrats

Quiz 14

Knowall's answer: Scapula – it's a bone not an organ
1. Acre is a unit of area, not length
2. Bourbon is French – the rest are English royal dynasties
3. Pilot officer is in the air force – the others are naval ranks
4. Cotton is the only natural fibre
5. Zeus is a Greek god, the rest are Roman
6. Petra is a name – the rest are currencies
7. Hyena is the only one that is not a "big cat"
8. Ballet is an area of dance – the others are specific dances
9. Count is not a British aristocratic title
10. Buddhist – the others

are divisions of the Christian church
11. Tomato is the only fruit – the rest are vegetables
12. Braque was an artist – the rest were classical composers
13. Orion is a constellation, not a planet
14. Sherry is a fortified wine – the others are spirits
15. Bulls (Chicago) play basketball – the others are American Football teams
16. Paris is the only national capital
17. *Gigi* was written by Lerner and Loewe – the rest were by Rodgers and Hammerstein
18. Pol Pot is the only one not to be assassinated
19. *Waterloo Sunset*, the only single not to make No. 1 for The Kinks
20. Tigon (cross between tiger and lion) exists – the others are mythical creatures
21. Beethoven was deaf – all the rest were or are blind
22. Montana is a US state, not an Indian tribe
23. Grace Kelly died in a car crash – the others died in plane crashes
24. Everton is in Liverpool – the rest are London soccer clubs
25. Franz Léhar composed *The Merry Widow* – the

ANSWERS

others were operettas by Gilbert and Sullivan
26. Taboo is a Polynesian word – the others are derived from India
27. Helen Mirren was never a TV "Avenger"
28. *Great Eastern* was a Brunel ship – the rest are famous trains
29. Aria is for a solo voice or instrument – the others involve more than one musician
30. The mammoth was not a dinosaur

Quiz 15

Knowall's answer: Tears
1. 21
2. To take blood away from the heart
3. Cells
4. The tongue
5. Carbon dioxide
6. 3
7. The fontanelle
8. The kidneys
9. An extra chromosome
10. The larynx

11. In the ears (bones)
12. The large intestine
13. Bile
14. The lymph glands
15. Vitamin D
16. Sebum
17. Oestrogen, progesterone
18. A follicle
19. Bone
20. A dark pigment found mainly in skin and hair
21. The eye
22. The uterus (womb)
23. Four
24. German measles (rubella)
25. The centre of the tongue
26. Tooth enamel
27. Insulin
28. Period pains
29. The optic nerve
30. Valium

Quiz 16

Knowall's answer: A nerve
1. The liver
2. The opium poppy
3. The grey matter is nerve cells, the white matter is nerve endings
4. 23 seconds
5. The pituitary gland
6. Red and green
7. 15 million
8. AB
9. Orthodontics
10. 12
11. 6 metres (20ft)
12. 18 days
13. The liver
14. 4.5 litres (9.5 pints)
15. Males

16. About 3lb (1.35kg)
17. 40 weeks
18. 100,000
19. Vitamin C
20. LSD
21. They are all bones in the arm
22. Minerals
23. Capillaries
24. Breathe and swallow
25. It helps build bones
26. The lower jawbone
27. Hydrochloric acid
28. 500 million
29. A motor neuron
30. Brunettes

Quiz 17

Knowall's answer: Smell
1. 22
2. Piles
3. On the soles of your feet (they are warts)
4. The hyoid bone
5. Baldness
6. The septum
7. White blood cells
8. About 1.9 square metres (20 square feet)
9. Sinuses
10. The Fallopian tubes
11. The femur (thigh bone), about 48cm (19in) in a man of average height
12. Veins
13. Dirt
14. 12: 7 pairs attached to the sternum and 5 "false" pairs
15. O
16. Windpipe
17. The making of artificial limbs and related

appliances
18. To remove waste material from the blood
19. 32
20. Gluteus maximus (the buttock)
21. The eyes
22. The collar bone
23. Red blood cells
24. Aspirin
25. The coccyx
26. Penicillin
27. Keratin
28. The Achilles tendon
29. The shin
30. Toenail

Quiz 18

Knowall's answer: Libra
1. Alchemy
2. Nostradamus
3. Tarot cards
4. The sphinx
5. Icarus
6. Kali
7. Beowulf
8. American Indians
9. The Knights Templar
10. The Gorgons
11. Ulster
12. El Dorado
13. The Freemasons
14. Diana
15. Valkyries
16. Astrology
17. Osiris
18. Jason's Voyage of the Argonauts
19. King Arthur
20. The Amazons
21. The Mayas
22. Atlantis
23. The Black Mass

ANSWERS

24. Fire, water, air and earth
25. Metaphysics
26. Aleister Crowley
27. Apollo
28. Inuit (Eskimos)
29. King of the Gods
30. Nemesis

Quiz 19

Knowall's answer: Greek
1. St Patrick
2. Nirvana
3. Barabbas
4. Teacher
5. 6 January ("Twelfth Night")
6. Brahmin (or Brahman)
7. Darius, King of the Medes and Persians
8. The Queen
9. Jehovah's Witnesses
10. The Koran
11. Nebuchadnezzar, after he had sacked Jerusalem
12. Defender of the Faith
13. Buddha
14. Early English
15. They turn towards Mecca
16. Saturday
17. "Thou shalt not kill"
18. Vatican City (the world's smallest country)
19. A *fatwa(h)*
20. Exodus
21. John the Baptist
22. *War Cry*
23. Christianity (Jesus)
24. The Inquisition
25. Japan
26. Tax collector
27. Five loaves and two fishes

28. Amritsar
29. 66 (39 in the Old Testament and 27 in the New)
30. Amen

Quiz 20

Knowall's answer: The Commandments stated: "Thou shalt commit adultery"
1. Shia (these are also called Sunnite and Shi'ite)
2. Ian Paisley
3. Bar Mitzvah
4. Swiss (they are known as the Swiss Guard)
5. They are encouraged never to cut their hair
6. The Druses (or Druzes)
7. Jeremiah
8. The Quakers
9. Minarets
10. 95
11. Jamaica
12. A theocracy
13. They are entitled to dye their hair red
14. St Denis
15. The Jesuits

16. Confucius
17. 20th (1920)
18. Lion
19. Miles Coverdale
20. Karma
21. Archbishop of Cracow
22. A bracelet of steel (worn on the right arm)
23. The Salvation Army
24. 7th
25. Ivory Coast: the cathedral's in the new capital of Yamoussoukro
26. The pig
27. Desmond Tutu
28. Hasidic Jews
29. Lourdes
30. French Protestants

Quiz 21

Knowall's answer: Henry Hudson
1. Waterloo, 1815
2. The Black Death (bubonic plague)
3. Karl Marx
4. Dunkirk
5. Julius Caesar
6. Cardinal Mazarin
7. The Matterhorn
8. Marco Polo
9. Sir Walter Raleigh
10. Order of the Garter
11. 1851
12. Attila the Hun
13. 4 July 1776
14. Captain Alfred Dreyfus
15. The *Mayflower*
16. Jean-Paul Marat
17. El Cid (Rodrigo Diaz de Bivar)
18. Captain Charles Cunningham Boycott

19. The Long March
20. Fireships
21. Dropped first A-bomb (on Hiroshima)
22. Texas
23. Admiral Lord Nelson
24. Queen Boudicca (Boadicea)
25. Alcock and Brown
26. Bartolomew Diaz
27. General Charles de Gaulle
28. Gerardus Mercator (Gerhard Kremer)
29. The Pinkerton Men
30. Emperor Nero

Quiz 22

Knowall's answer: Garibaldi
1. Vietnam
2. Captain Robert Jenkins
3. Nuremberg
4. Carthage
5. The Napoleonic Code
6. Shakespeare and Cervantes
7. The election of rival Popes (Clement VII and Urban VI)
8. Genghis Khan's
9. The Statue of Liberty
10. Khartoum
11. The Dalai Lama (from Tibet)
12. Robert O'Hare Burke and W. J. Wills
13. Dresden
14. Suleiman the Magnificent
15. Leon Trotsky
16. Thomas à Becket's murder at Canterbury

ANSWERS

17. The Wall Street Crash
18. The taxi-cabs
19. Sir Francis Drake
20. Mungo Park
21. Rajiv Gandhi
22. William Pitt the Younger
23. Richard the Lionheart
24. The *Lusitania*
25. King Nebuchadnezzar II
26. Battle of Lepanto
27. 1999
28. The sale of alcohol (Prohibition)
29. The Domesday Book
30. Ned Kelly

Quiz 23

Knowall's answer:
Plebians (plebs)
1. Hastings, 1066
2. The Eiffel Tower, Paris
3. The Magna Carta
4. 1989
5. Spartacus
6. Agadir
7. Mikhail Gorbachev
8. Queen Anne
9. Brian Boru
10. Russia and Japan
11. Panama
12. Spain's blockade of Gibraltar
13. Omar Khayyam
14. General Galtieri
15. Chairman Mao Tse-tung
16. Nicolae Ceausescu (Romania)
17. The slave trade
18. Mohandas Gandhi (The Mahatma)
19. The Franco-Prussian War

20. Vaclav Havel
21. Zulfikar Ali Bhutto
22. Francisco Pizarro
23. 1981
24. The Great Wall of China
25. Solidarity
26. Tulip bulbs
27. Constantinople
28. Bonnie Prince Charlie's
29. 1849
30. The Gulf War

Quiz 24

Knowall's answer:
The Duke of Wellington's
1. The 15th century
2. Jo Grimond
3. Philip II of Spain (with wife Mary I)
4. *Punch*
5. 400 million
6. Richard I (the Lionheart)
7. Westland
8. Clement Attlee, from 1945 to 1951
9. Lieutenant
10. All paper to bear a royal arms watermark
11. George III
12. Greenham Common
13. Catherine of Aragon
14. Income tax
15. Hanover
16. Making Victoria Cross medals
17. Captain Blood
18. The Ulster Peace Agreement
19. Black Rod
20. George II (Battle of Dettingen, 1743)

21. London's National Gallery extension
22. William the Conqueror
23. The *Daily Mail* (1900)
24. Norman Lamont
25. Lord Louis Mountbatten
26. The Regency
27. Lord Home (Alec Douglas-Home)
28. 19 years (1568-1587)
29. The Falklands War (1992)
30. Catherine Parr

Quiz 25

Knowall's answer:
Dancing
1. Culloden
2. David Lloyd George
3. Edward (V and VIII)
4. John Knox
5. O'Connell Street Post Office
6. Stella Rimington (MI5)
7. The English Crown (Richard III to Henry VII)
8. *Lady Ghislaine*
9. Butter Osborne

10. John of Gaunt
11. The Territorial Army
12. Caernarvon
13. The Yangtse (China)
14. Scone in Scotland
15. Perkin Warbeck
16. The *Torrey Canyon*
17. "Remember"
18. Sir Thomas More
19. 1946
20. Egypt
21. Elizabeth I
22. Martello towers
23. World War 1
24. Gibraltar
25. Copenhagen
26. He fell off the lavatory
27. The Prince of Wales (later Edward VII)
28. An inch
29. Buckingham Palace
30. Caroline of Brunswick

Quiz 26

Knowall's answer:
King Zog of Albania (in London exile)
1. Alfred The Great
2. Maastrict Treaty
3. James Callaghan
4. Ben Jonson
5. His crown
6. D-Day commemorations in France
7. The Cod War
8. Prince Albert
9. The General Strike
10. Diana, Princess of Wales
11. James I
12. First stately home opened to the public
13. Rhodesia

14. Birmingham
15. Gog and Magog
16. The Gregorian Calendar
17. IRA bombings
18. 9 years, 6 months (1935-1945)
19. 137,000 (1787-1852)
20. Electricity was generated
21. Margaret Thatcher
22. They were brothers
23. Edward Heath
24. George VI (in 1939)
25. Chairman (leader) of the Labour Party
26. William Penn
27. The community charge (poll tax)
28. George V, Edward VIII and George VI
29. Fourth wife Anne of Cleves
30. Holyrood Palace

Quiz 27

Knowall's answer:
Richard M. Nixon
1. Mike Tyson
2. The Ku Klux Klan
3. Italy
4. The Marine Corps
5. Manhattan Island
6. Jesse James
7. Syphilis
8. Atlanta
9. Joseph Pulitzer
10. Molasses (sugar)
11. Scandinavia
12. Sitting Bull and Crazy Horse
13. George Washington
14. Spain
15. First English child born in the New World

16. Washington, Jefferson, Teddy Roosevelt, Lincoln
17. The "Flying Fortress"
18. Wounded Knee
19. Benjamin Franklin
20. Horses
21. Booker T. Washington
22. Pearl Harbor, Hawaii
23. Arkansas
24. Virginia
25. Patty Hearst
26. The Mexican War
27. Henry Ford's
28. Cornelius Vanderbilt
29. Princess Pocahontas
30. William McKinley

Quiz 28

Knowall's answer:
John D. Rockefeller
1. The Alamo
2. General Robert E. Lee
3. The United States Constitution
4. John Dillinger
5. Harvard
6. Blackbeard (Edward Teach)
7. *The Sun*
8. William Henry Harrison
9. 1493
10. The Bay of Pigs
11. Beirut
12. Mormon founder Brigham Young
13. Martin Luther King
14. 8 years
15. The Liberty Bell
16. Franklin D. Roosevelt
17. Execution of 20 "witches"
18. President Abraham

Lincoln
19. Annie Oakley
20. The Pacific Ocean
21. Lee Harvey Oswald
22. Joe McCarthy
23. 3 million
24. Charles Lindbergh
25. San Francisco Bay
26. The minimum hourly wage
27. Daniel Boone
28. The Texas Rangers
29. Ellis Island
30. Theodore "Teddy" Roosevelt

Quiz 29

Knowall's answer:
Pudding Lane
1. Lockerbie
2. Krakatoa
3. San Francisco
4. Tenerife, Canary Islands
5. York Minster
6. The White Star Line
7. The *Hindenburg*
8. Chernobyl
9. Bradford City
10. Lynmouth
11. Shot down by a Soviet

fighter
12. Lisbon
13. Failure of the potato crop
14. Pompeii
15. *The Herald of Free Enterprise*
16. The Busby Babes
17. Aberfan
18. An exploding gas tanker
19. Bubonic plague
20. *Piper Alpha*
21. Heysel and Hillsborough
22. The *Marchioness*
23. Waco
24. Thalidomide
25. Clapham Junction
26. *Exxon Valdez*
27. Grand Hotel, Brighton
28. 1987 (October)
29. Floods
30. The *Mary Rose*

Quiz 30

Knowall's answer:
Discotheque
1. A surveying instrument
2. A tail
3. Random Access Memory
4. The python
5. Joan of Arc
6. Montana
7. South Africa's Afrikaners (Boers)
8. Two-thirds plus one
9. Joseph Lister (*circa* 1865)
10. The Dardanelles
11. First hot-air balloon flight (1783)
12. The penny-farthing

ANSWERS

13. 12
14. 98.4°F (36.9°C)
15. Louis XIV of France
16. Lord of the Flies
17. Bonsai
18. The truffle
19. Into exile on St Helena
20. Ritual suicide
21. Balaclava
22. 1801
23. The world's first heart transplant patient (1967)
24. San Marino (10th century)
25. The Golden Gate
26. Glass
27. Oberammergau
28. Oliver Cromwell
29. Quebec, Canada
30. A bat

Quiz 31

Knowall's answer: Necker
1. France: The Jean Bernard cave is 1,494m (4,900ft) deep
2. A huge tidal wave caused by an earthquake or volcanic activity
3. The Bass Strait
4. A "twister"
5. Antarctica
6. The Scottish Highlands (it's traditionally Achnashellach)
7. A flat-topped, steep-sided rock outcrop, notably in the south-western USA
8. New Guinea
9. Visibility in fog is less than 1km; more than 1km is classed as mist
10. Off the west coast of the Isle of Wight
11. Africa and Asia
12. Estimates vary: you're right if you said either the Gobi or the Arabian
13. The Beaufort Scale
14. A typhoon
15. The Volga
16. Canada
17. Moraine (rocks, stones and other debris carried and deposited by glaciers)
18. Botswana (mainly) and Namibia
19. Rock
20. Brown coal
21. Up the west coast of southern Africa, towards the equator
22. Youth, maturity and old age (or young, mature and old)
23. The Mojave Desert
24. Groynes
25. The Caucasus
26. Antarctica
27. South of the Bering Sea in the northern Pacific, running in an arc between Russia and Alaska
28. Limestone
29. The vast region of coniferous forest in Russia (and also North America) between the tundra to the north and the deciduous forest and steppes to the south
30. The Loire, at 1,020km (635 miles)

Quiz 32

Knowall's answer: Volcanoes
1. Michael Fish
2. A wadi
3. Geysers
4. Mt St Helens
5. Faults caused by movements in the Earth's crust
6. Mt Everest
7. In Hebei province, northern China
8. Surtsey
9. Kentucky
10. Inner core (parts of the Earth from the surface to the centre)
11. Loch Lomond
12. Continental drift
13. The Gulf Stream
14. That the melting ice-caps will lead to further rises in sea levels – and they would effectively "sink" beneath the waves
15. 371km/h (231mph) at Mt Washington, New Hampshire, USA on 12

April 1934 – three times as strong as hurricane force
16. Victoria Falls, on the Zambezi
17. Mt Fuji (also called Fuyi-San or Fuyi-yama)
18. The total energy released by an earthquake
19. He was surveyor-general of India
20. The (South) Atlantic
21. The Great Rift Valley
22. The Pacific
23. The monsoon
24. Australia
25. Longshore drift
26. 58°C (136.4°F) at Al Aziziyah, Libya, on 13 September 1922
27. The Andes
28. Cyclones
29. The Severn
30. Lake Chad

Quiz 33

Knowall's answer: Long Island
1. The White House
2. Huron
3. Wyoming
4. St Louis
5. Ontario
6. Alaska
7. Hawaii
8. Edmonton
9. The Colorado River
10. California (30,895,000)
11. The St Lawrence Seaway
12. Massachusetts
13. Labrador

14. The Rio Grande
15. Denmark
16. California and Florida
17. The Chinook
18. Chicago
19. Great Bear Lake and Great Slave Lake
20. New Jersey
21. Russia (Siberia)
22. Amerigo Vespucci (1454-1512)
23. Maryland
24. The 39th
25. St Pierre & Miquelon (an overseas department of France)
26. Arlington
27. Baffin Island
28. New Orleans
29. Quebec (Canadian provinces from west to east)
30. $7 million ($7.2 million to be exact)

Quiz 34

Knowall's answer:
Violence at two soccer World Cup qualifying matches
1. The Amazon
2. Panama (countries of the Central American isthmus from north to south)
3. Lake Titicaca
4. Jamaica
5. Chile
6. Bolivia or Paraguay
7. Haiti
8. Venezuela
9. Yucatan
10. Barbados

11. São Paulo
12. Havana
13. Ecuador
14. Grenada
15. Aztec
16. France
17. Argentina
18. Brazil (Portuguese), Guyana (English), Surinam (Dutch), French Guiana (French)
19. St Lucia
20. Peru
21. The Malvinas (*Islas Malvinas*)
22. Acapulco
23. Colombia
24. The USA and Britain
25. Tierra del Fuego
26. French Guiana
27. A snake
28. *Rio de la Plata* (River Plate)
29. Curaçao
30. 1914

Quiz 35

Knowall's answer:
Mount Kilimanjaro
1. Nigeria (115,700,000)
2. 9
3. Mali
4. Rwanda and Burundi (the principal tribes)
5. Stanley and Livingstone
6. Morocco
7. Somali Republic
8. Limpopo
9. Cairo (6,800,000)
10. Zambia: the only one without a coast
11. Kenya
12. Zambezi

13. Ghana
14. Liberia = liberty (It was founded in the early 19th century as an American colony for freed black slaves returning to Africa)
15. Tanzania
16. The Atlas Mountains
17. Ethiopia
18. Table Mountain
19. Tunisia
20. Khartoum
21. Ivory Coast
22. The Congo (or Zaïre) – 4,670km (2,900 miles)
23. Sudan (9th in the world)
24. The River Niger
25. 3 (Guinea, Guinea-Bissau and Equatorial Guinea)
26. Egypt
27. The rand
28. Mozambique (Madagascar and Mauritius are also correct: both are considered parts of Africa)
29. Lake Victoria, Africa's largest
30. Namibia

Quiz 36

Knowall's answer:
Advance Australia Fair
1. Tasmania
2. Bikini
3. New South Wales (Australian states)
4. Cook Strait
5. Ayers Rock

6. Port Moresby
7. Melbourne
8. Nauru
9. Wallaby
10. *The Piano*
11. The Great Barrier Reef
12. Fiji
13. Canberra
14. The Maoris
15. Opals
16. Samoa
17. Darwin
18. Wellington
19. The Great Dividing Range
20. Tuna
21. Perth
22. They are all French Overseas Territories
23. Sydney
24. Tonga
25. Gold
26. Pelau (Belau)
27. Sheep
28. The Flying Doctor
29. Pitcairn
30. Lake Eyre

Quiz 37

Knowall's answer:
Islamabad
1. The Khyber Pass
2. Tokyo, Japan

ANSWERS

3. The Dead Sea at –400m (–1,312ft)
4. India
5. Siam
6. Trans-Siberian Railway
7. Krakatoa, created by a volcanic eruption in 1883, is west of Java
8. The Ganges
9. K2 (Chogori) at 8,610m (28,250ft)
10. Shanghai (8,930,000)
11. 20%
12. Honshu and Hokkaido
13. Qatar
14. Ho-Chi Minh City
15. Bhutan
16. Kuala Lumpur
17. Nepal (its flag is triangular)
18. The Yellow River
19. Mongolia
20. The River Jordan
21. Punjab
22. Sri Lanka
23. Calcutta (all the rest are national capital cities)
24. Mecca
25. Singapore
26. Iraq and Iran

27. Yokohama (3,288,000)
28. India
29. Tibet
30. Named after Philip II (1527-98) by the Spanish colonialists

Quiz 38

Knowall's answer: Liechtenstein
1. Amsterdam, Bruges or Stockholm
2. Montenegro
3. The Urals
4. Andorra
5. Vienna
6. Denmark
7. The Balearics
8. San Marino or Vatican City
9. Mt Athos (Holy Mountain) in northern Greece
10. The River Danube
11. Madrid
12. Poland
13. Tiber (Tiberius)
14. Cork
15. Romania
16. Karl-Marx-Stadt
17. Britain (then Iceland and Ireland)
18. The Netherlands (Germany's neighbours going "clockwise")
19. Geneva
20. It's a powerful Arctic Ocean current with a tidal race that funnels through a channel in the Lofoten Islands
21. Ukraine (France is now third)

22. The Apennines
23. The mistral
24. Barcelona
25. Leningrad
26. France and Italy
27. The Hague
28. The Camargue
29. Finland
30. Milan

Quiz 39

Knowall's answer: Land's End and John O'Groats
1. Birmingham
2. All 10
3. Basalt
4. Anglesey
5. Gravesend
6. Larne
7. The Cotswolds
8. The Humber
9. Glen More
10. Lake Windermere
11. Felixstowe
12. Longleat
13. They are the smaller Channel Islands
14. The Tower Colliery
15. Derby: all the rest are county towns (Matlock is the county town of Derbyshire)
16. Salisbury
17. The Severn
18. The Wash
19. Osborne House
20. The 6th century
21. Scafell Pike (*not* Scafell)
22. Aylesbury
23. Lough Neagh
24. Kent (counties along the south coast of England)

25. Skye
26. Horses
27. Wallsend
28. The Potteries
29. Lowestoft, Suffolk
30. Douglas

Quiz 40

Knowall's answer: Tyburn Tree (a gallows)
1. Fruit and vegetables
2. London's first underground railway
3. The Strand
4. London City Airport, Docklands
5. St Katharine Dock
6. Nelson's Column, Trafalgar Square
7. Carnaby Street
8. Lambeth
9. Regent's Park
10. Bloomsbury
11. St Bartholomew's (Barts)
12. The Duke of Wellington
13. The Globe
14. 11 Downing Street
15. Hungerford Bridge
16. The Isle of Dogs
17. Rotten Row
18. Westminster Cathedral (Catholic)
19. Aluminium
20. The Great Exhibition of 1851
21. The George Inn, Southwark
22. Victoria Park
23. Wembley Stadium
24. John Nash
25. The Temple, Middle Temple, Inner Temple

26. Aldgate, Aldersgate, Bishopsgate, Ludgate, Newgate
27. Billingsgate
28. London Bridge
29. Lord's
30. Whitehall and Westminster Palaces

Quiz 41

Knowall's answer: William IV (British sovereigns in chronological order)

1. Gerald Ford (US presidents)
2. Epsilon (Greek alphabet)
3. Wimbledon (FA Cup winners to 1988)
4. Saturn (planets in order from the Sun)
5. Kilometre
6. 35 (arithmetical progression)
7. November (NATO alphabet)
8. Atlanta (Olympic venues to 1996)
9. Octagon (even-sided shapes to 8)
10. Dover (UK shipping forecast areas)
11. Russian (world's most spoken languages)
12. Carbon (No 6 in the table of elements)
13. Scorpio (signs of the zodiac)
14. Wilson (postwar British prime ministers)
15. Hurricane (strongest wind on the Beaufort Scale)
16. John Paul II (the present Pope)
17. P (letters on top line of typewriter/computer keyboard)
18. Akihito (Japanese emperors)
19. Semiquaver
20. Brosnan (Pierce – James Bonds on film)
21. *She Loves You* (Beatles' first singles)
22. Gorbachev (general secretaries of the USSR)
23. Brazil (World Cup winners to 1994)
24. Captain (British army ranks)
25. Japan (population size)
26. Southwark (Thames road bridges going downstream)
27. Chirac (recent French presidents)
28. Ted Hughes (Poets Laureate)
29. Colorado (US states in alphabetical order)
30. Violet (colours of the rainbow)

Quiz 42

Knowall's answer: The Hunter

1. The Big Bang
2. Copernicus
3. National Aeronautics and Space Administration
4. *Sputnik* 1
5. Galileo
6. The Pole Star
7. Viking 1
8. The closest star to Earth
9. The Northern Lights
10. A supernova
11. Venus
12. A collapsed star
13. MIR
14. Jupiter
15. Helen Sharman
16. Neptune
17. The Great Bear
18. First animal in space (a Russian dog)
19. The Milky Way
20. Apollo 13
21. The first man to walk in space
22. The *Challenger* mission
23. Yuri Gagarin, 1961
24. Ptolemy
25. Mercury
26. *Columbia*, 1977
27. Buzz Aldrin
28. 27 days
29. Stephen Hawking
30. 1986

Quiz 43

Knowall's answer: The electric filament light

1. It was the world's first nuclear-powered vessel
2. Alexandra Palace, London
3. An apple falling to the ground
4. $E = mc^2$
5. On the guillotine
6. Red
7. An adding machine
8. Alexander Graham Bell
9. Sonar
10. The pressure cooker
11. Sewing machines
12. A catalyst
13. Pasteurisation
14. Self-Contained Underwater Breathing Apparatus
15. Benjamin Franklin
16. The Philosopher's Stone
17. Roman roads
18. Hydrogen
19. Lewis E. Waterman
20. The Royal Society
21. Nylon
22. John Boyd Dunlop
23. Remington
24. Tin
25. X-rays
26. Archimedes
27. The phonograph
28. World's first general-purpose computer
29. Euclid
30. A Channel tunnel

Quiz 44

Knowall's answer: Auguste and Louis Lumière

1. The Polaroid camera
2. Electrical activity in the brain

ANSWERS

3. Aluminium
4. Thomas Alva Edison
5. Types of loudspeaker
6. Conduction, convection and radiation
7. One million years
8. Charles Darwin
9. The dial telephone
10. Samuel Colt
11. That between pressure and volume
12. Helium
13. The first electric battery
14. Solid, liquid, and gas
15. Nickel
16. The ohm
17. Apple Computer
18. Radio detection and ranging
19. –273°C
20. Marie Curie (1903 and 1911)
21. Sulphuric acid
22. Starting a fire
23. Guglielmo Marconi (1901)
24. Printing
25. Salt
26. Elisha Otis
27. A water-lifting auger
28. Copper and zinc
29. Alfred Nobel
30. Animal behaviour in its natural environment

Quiz 45

**Knowall's answer:
The electric telegraph**

1. The hovercraft
2. Single-lens reflex
3. An endoscope
4. Frank Whittle
5. The barometer

6. Werner von Braun
7. The machine-gun
8. James Watt
9. The photocopier
10. The world's first submarine
11. Jean Bernard Léon Foucault
12. The integrated circuit (semiconductor)
13. The atomic bomb
14. An astrolabe
15. IBM (International Business Machines)
16. The first practical working steam engine
17. A hologram
18. The flushing toilet
19. The Hawker Harrier
20. Magnetism and electricity
21. The printing press
22. Abraham Darby
23. The vacuum flask
24. The thermometer
25. Jacques Cousteau
26. To crack German codes
27. The Turin Shroud
28. Clive Sinclair
29. Flintlock
30. The first combine harvester

Quiz 46

Knowall's answer: For victims of road traffic accidents

1. As a cleaning agent
2. Tupolev-144 ("Konkordski")
3. 1839
4. Opel
5. Richard Trevithick

6. The *Mallard*
7. The Austin Motor Company
8. Le Mans, France
9. The *Sir Winston Churchill*
10. Igor Sikorsky
11. SS *Great Britain*
12. Aston Martin
13. First steam locomotive in the USA
14. The Jaguar Car Company
15. 1869
16. Cadillac
17. London and Paris
18. Rolls-Royce
19. Brighton
20. Morris Garages
21. Burrell
22. BMW
23. The Galaxy
24. TGVs (*Trains très grand vitesse*)
25. Ferraris
26. 15 million
27. Sir Henry Segrave
28. Amtrak
29. France, Britain and

West Germany
30. The discovery of gold in Australia

Quiz 47

**Knowall's answer:
The *Lusitania***

1. The world's first steam railway
2. Karl Benz
3. The Austin Seven
4. 1904
5. The Suez Canal
6. Chrysler
7. First American killed in an air crash
8. Roll on, roll off (car ferry)
9. 1968
10. Oldsmobile
11. 3 million
12. A Ford Mustang
13. Burial of their ashes in space
14. A Channel tunnel
15. Baltimore
16. 2,900
17. Trolleybuses
18. The Roaring Forties
19. Bubble cars
20. Peking (Beijing)
21. *The Flying Scotsman*
22. Tilbury
23. Daimler
24. Steam
25. George Mortimer Pullman
26. The *QE2*
27. The De Lorean
28. A fifth terminal
29. The Advanced Passenger Train (APT)
30. Thomas Edison

Quiz 48

Knowall's answer:
Ettore Bugatti
1. London and Bristol
2. Tea clippers
3. Gottlieb Daimler's
4. An autogiro
5. Mercedes
6. "Leaves on the line"
7. Canals
8. A mechanic
9. It carried the world's first air mail
10. The *Queen Elizabeth*
11. Donald Campbell
12. British Airways
13. Honda
14. *Sanspareil*
15. The de Havilland Comet
16. David Dunbar Buick
17. Louis Blériot
18. Electricity
19. Penny-farthings
20. Bentley Motors
21. The Empire State Building
22. The Ford Popular
23. The Panama Canal
24. The Victoria Line
25. Skoda
26. 545
27. The Morgan Motor Company
28. Hobby-horses
29. The Morris Oxford
30. Whaling

Quiz 49

Knowall's answer: Koala
1. Humans
2. The elephant
3. Platypus or echnida
4. Four
5. Hippopotamus
6. Water buffalo
7. None
8. The gorilla
9. Marsupials
10. Bears
11. Orang-utan (Malay)
12. Sloth and/or the wolverine (also called the glutton)
13. Lodges
14. The Goliath bird-eating spider
15. The blue whale
16. Bactrian (a dromedary has one)
17. The giraffe
18. Hair
19. 750
20. The cheetah
21. Goat
22. Bamboo shoots
23. The bat
24. A jenny
25. A snake
26. "Jumbo"
27. Apes and monkeys
28. The wildebeest
29. 42
30. Zoology

Quiz 50

Knowall's answer:
The USA
1. The cow
2. India
3. Blood
4. Hibernate
5. Lizards
6. Anaconda is the heaviest, python the longest

7. 8
8. The bear
9. Fat
10. Male donkey and female horse
11. The wolf
12. Two dogs and a cat
13. A monitor lizard, the Komodo dragon
14. The Barbary ape (still found on Gibraltar)
15. Amphibians
16. "Tarka"
17. The chamois, a goat-like mountain antelope of southern Europe
18. Ridgeback
19. Spiders (arachnids)
20. A joey
21. The llama
22. He was crossed-eyed
23. 30cm (12in)
24. The zebra
25. The rhinoceros
26. Deer (on the antlers)
27. A mongoose
28. The springbok
29. The mosquito
30. To smell the air

Quiz 51

Knowall's answer:
Cardinal
1. The otter
2. Beetles
3. The polecat
4. A small deer
5. "Toad" (of Toad Hall)
6. The red deer
7. The adder (or viper)
8. Rabbits
9. The honey bee
10. A sett
11. Pigmy shrew
12. The black rat
13. The dormouse
14. The badger
15. A hare
16. Mink and coypu (now eradicated)
17. Ermine
18. Pups
19. To attract mates
20. Fish
21. A jack or pickerel
22. The Sargasso Sea in the western Atlantic
23. Toad
24. Lynx
25. A butterfly
26. Because it eats greenfly, a garden pest
27. The brush
28. A lion and a unicorn
29. A doe or hind
30. The Isle of Wight

Quiz 52

Knowall's answer:
Capuchin monkeys
1. The ostrich
2. The wandering albatross

ANSWERS

3. The bald eagle
4. 24,000
5. The bee hummingbird
6. The swift
7. New Guinea
8. To help grind food
9. The wren
10. The dunnock
11. The puffin
12. The cuckoo
13. Tits
14. The goldcrest
15. The avocet
16. The kiwi
17. Peewit or lapwing
18. Geese
19. The magpie
20. The pelican
21. Pebbles
22. They don't
23. Grey
24. Ravens
25. Uganda
26. The blackbird
27. Homing pigeons
28. The condor
29. The kookaburra
30. The road runner

Quiz 53

Knowall's answer:
"Terrible lizard"
1. Fish
2. Palaeontology
3. Tyrannosaurus rex
4. Sabre-toothed tiger
5. It had the longest tail
6. Mammoth (and/or mastodon)
7. A fish
8. Polishing or manufacture of dynamite
9. Brachiosaurus

10. Three
11. It was a flying dinosaur
12. In the sea
13. To lose body heat
14. Reptiles and birds
15. The Jurassic
16. Coal
17. Eggs
18. Dino
19. 65 million years
20. A sail on its back
21. Stegosaurus (0.004 of 1% of its computed body weight)
22. Megalosaurus
23. Oxfordshire
24. On its "thumbs"
25. Ammonites
26. Claws
27. Sedimentary rocks
28. The "Roc"
29. Eggs
30. The Triassic

Quiz 54

Knowall's answer: Orchids
1. The willow
2. North America
3. Chlorophyll
4. Algae

5. The maple
6. A fern
7. Yews
8. The potato
9. The cork oak
10. Eucalyptus
11. Marigold
12. Papyrus
13. Bamboo
14. Beech nuts
15. The canopy
16. The rowan
17. Vitamin C
18. Amber
19. Mushroom/toadstool
20. Salt water
21. It is square
22. Cacao (also used for cocao)
23. Cactus
24. Bristlecone pines
25. Samphire
26. The banyan
27. The douglas fir
28. The hazel
29. The coconut
30. The wattle or bottle-brush

Quiz 55

Knowall's answer: Rice
1. Gladioli
2. Evergreen leaves
3. Rayon
4. Moss
5. Anise or aniseed
6. The tap root
7. The red rose
8. Breadfruit
9. The crocus
10. Lily
11. The mandrake
12. Grasses

13. The elm
14. Roses
15. The thistle
16. Tequila
17. Oregano
18. Asia
19. Pollen
20. The lime
21. Lilies
22. Acetylene
23. The daffodil
24. Reindeer moss
25. Raffia
26. Lily-of-the-valley
27. Artichokes
28. It has many flowers on one stem
29. Snails
30. The mulberry

Quiz 56

Knowall's answer:
The gunwhale
1. It plays dead
2. 5 cents and 10 cents
3. His bow and arrow
4. American
5. John Brown
6. The Tees (Caldron Snout)
7. *Martin Chuzzlewit*
8. 18 inches (45.7cm)
9. The dragonfly
10. Captain Hastings
11. The ankle
12. The Red Crescent
13. Earth
14. Plymouth (the Hoe)
15. Distress
16. 12
17. Mice
18. Belgium
19. The George Cross

20. Multiple sclerosis
21. Nine of diamonds
22. None
23. Tokyo
24. Henry V
25. Whitworth
26. *Danny Boy*
27. Colonel Tom Parker
28. The Silver Ghost
29. A runcible spoon
30. Skye

Quiz 57

Knowall's answer:
Brendan Behan
1. Charlotte
2. An asp
3. Pinkie
4. *The Borough*
5. John Webster
6. Horatio Hornblower
7. W. B. Yeats, George Bernard Shaw or Samuel Beckett
8. *The Pilgrim's Progress* by John Bunyan
9. *Anna Karenina*
10. *The Adventures of Huckleberry Finn*
11. Eppie
12. The University of Hull
13. Mrs Malaprop
14. Anthony Trollope (in the "Palliser" series of novels)
15. *The Go-Between*
16. Mr Darcy
17. A. S. Byatt
18. *Moby-Dick* by Herman Melville
19. Bram Stoker for *Dracula*
20. Lewis Carroll

21. Henry James
22. *The Importance of Being Earnest*
23. *Lark Rise to Candleford*
24. *Nightmare Abbey*
25. *Black Beauty* by Anna Sewell
26. Mary Renault
27. *She Stoops to Conquer*
28. Meg, Beth, Jo and Amy
29. *The Naked Lunch*
30. *The Mayor of Casterbridge*

Quiz 58

Knowall's answer:
Education
1. *Catch-22*
2. *The Iliad* or *The Odyssey*
3. William Cobbett, *Rural Rides*
4. Exmoor
5. Somerville and Ross
6. *Three Men in a Boat*
7. Don Quixote
8. French
9. The Bloomsbury Group
10. Gertrude
11. Robert Burns
12. Alexander Solzhenitsyn
13. Georges Simenon
14. The sea
15. Emily Dickinson
16. *The Lord of the Rings*
17. *The Decameron* by Boccaccio
18. Dylan Thomas
19. *Robinson Crusoe* by Daniel Defoe
20. Sarah Gamp
21. *Frankenstein*
22. James Thurber

23. *Madame Bovary*
24. Robert Surtees
25. An albatross
26. James Kelman
27. William Wordsworth
28. A surgeon
29. *The Canterbury Tales* by Chaucer
30. T. S. Eliot

Quiz 59

Knowall's answer:
Alexander Pope
1. Arthur Miller
2. Heathcliff
3. *The Water-Babies*
4. Jim Hawkins
5. John Galsworthy, *The Forsyte Saga*
6. Mowgli
7. *Doctor Zhivago*
8. The Poldarks
9. *Vanity Fair*
10. Doris Lessing
11. Emma
12. Nathaniel Hawthorne
13. Percy Bysshe Shelley
14. Derek Walcott
15. *Around the World in Eighty Days*
16. Lawrence (Larry), Leslie and Margot
17. William Blake
18. *Wild Swans*
19. *Look Back in Anger*
20. Shylock
21. *Goblin Market*
22. Malcolm Bradbury
23. *High Fidelity* by Nick Hornby
24. Bruce Chatwin
25. Tom Stoppard
26. Estella

27. John Braine, *Room at the Top*
28. Melvyn Bragg
29. Thomas Gray
30. Raymond Carver

Quiz 60

Knowall's answer: His older brother Mycroft
1. John Grisham
2. *Casino Royale*
3. Gerald Seymour
4. Jack Ryan
5. Agatha Christie's
6. Ruth Rendell
7. Campbell Armstrong
8. Bernard Samson
9. Raymond Chandler
10. National Hunt jockey
11. Clive Cussler
12. Robert Harris
13. Tom Ripley
14. Wilkie Collins
15. Eddy Shah
16. Gavin Lyall
17. Lord Peter Wimsey and Bunter
18. Alistair Maclean
19. Eric Van Lustbader
20. Ellis Peters

ANSWERS

21. Raffles
22. Colin Dexter
23. Frederick Forsyth
24. Patricia Cornwell
25. *Prizzi's Honour*
26. Ross Macdonald
27. Hammond Innes
28. P. D. James
29. They contain the names of animals or birds
30. Jack Higgins

Knowall's answer:
Douglas Adams
1. Victor
2. *The Thing*
3. *Nautilus*
4. Johannes Kepler
5. *The Sentinel*
6. The Starship *Enterprise*
7. Winston Smith
8. *The Sandman* (1817)
9. Narnia
10. *The Land that Time Forgot* (1924)
11. William Morris
12. Father and son
13. H. G. Wells
14. A small pterodactyl
15. *Metropolis*
16. Dr Jekyll
17. Polish
18. The temperature at which books burn
19. Isaac Asimov
20. *The Novel of the Coming Century*
21. Jane Fonda
22. E. M. Forster
23. Orson Welles
24. John Wyndham
25. *Neuromancer*

26. Ming the Merciless, Emperor of Mongo
27. Passepartout
28. Middle Earth
29. *Drowned World* (1962)
30. *The Handmaid's Tale*

Quiz 62

Knowall's answer: *Irises*
1. Munnings or Stubbs
2. Titian
3. Hans Holbein the Younger
4. Degas
5. Norman Rockwell
6. Auguste Rodin
7. Cave paintings
8. *The Monarch of the Glen*
9. Pointillism
10. Van Dyck
11. Gouache
12. Frans Hals
13. The Pre-Raphaelite Brotherhood
14. Icon
15. Paul Gaugin
16. Leonardo da Vinci, The Louvre
17. The Renaissance
18. Pieter Bruegel
19. A triptych
20. Nicholas Hilliard
21. Tintoretto
22. The Bayeaux Tapestry
23. Padua
24. Botticelli
25. Majolica
26. Canaletto
27. J. M. W. Turner
28. Claude Monet
29. Gainsborough
30. W. Heath Robinson

Quiz 63

Knowall's answer: Birds
1. Michelangelo
2. Picasso
3. Expressionism
4. William Hogarth
5. Dutch
6. Lord Frederic Leighton
7. Illumination
8. Aubrey Beardsley
9. Rio de Janeiro
10. Wood engraving
11. Salvador Dali
12. John Constable
13. Frescoes
14. Toulouse-Lautrec
15. James Gillray
16. Van Gogh
17. El Greco
18. Richard Dadd
19. Barbara Hepworth
20. Primitive
21. Sir William Russell Flint
22. Lord Elgin
23. Rembrandt
24. Auguste Renoir (Jean Renoir)
25. Napoleon Bonaparte's
26. Dürer
27. Forging paintings
28. Tate Gallery (Sir Henry Tate of Tate & Lyle)
29. Those of Charles Dickens
30. Wedgwood

Quiz 64

Knowall's answer: The **Opera House**
1. The Bastille
2. Lambeth Palace

3. Chartwell
4. Glamis Castle
5. Cliveden
6. St Peter's, Rome
7. Balmoral
8. The Royal Pavilion, Brighton
9. The Reichstag
10. Quarry Bank Mill
11. Beaumaris
12. St Paul's Cathedral
13. Somerset House
14. The Taj Mahal
15. Richard Rogers
16. Tower of London
17. Glastonbury
18. The Canada Tower at Canary Wharf
19. Flatford Mill, Suffolk
20. The Golden Temple
21. Sir Walter Scott
22. Portmeirion
23. Northumberland
24. The "Bridge of Sighs"
25. Marlborough
26. Bury St Edmunds
27. The British Museum
28. Versailles, near Paris
29. Ludwig Mies van der Rohe
30. The Forbidden City

Knowall's answer: The Kodak Box Brownie
1. Terence Conran
2. Louis Comfort Tiffany
3. Bauhaus
4. The post-war Morris Minor
5. Cartier
6. 1876
7. Le Corbusier
8. Norman Hartnell
9. Barnes Wallis
10. Charles Rennie Mackintosh
11. Clarice Cliff
12. Edwin Lutyens
13. Lucky Strike
14. Rudolf Diesel
15. The Terry anglepoise lamp
16. 1889
17. Concorde
18. Vespa
19. Cristal Lalique
20. The London Underground map
21. Wilbur and Orville Wright

22. Honda
23. Eric Gill
24. Electrolux
25. Antonio Gaudi
26. Ferdinand Porsche
27. Laura Ashley
28. Clive Sinclair
29. Olivetti
30. William Morris

Quiz 66

Knowall's answer: 106 (1337–1453)
1. London (1863)
2. Metropolitan (1863)
3. *Hamlet*
4. Oxford (founded 1249)
5. Gruyère
6. The Prado
7. Canterbury (1071)
8. Julius Caesar
9. Victoria (63 years)
10. Henry VI (8 months)
11. William IV (64)
12. Gladstone (84)
13. Mercury
14. Automobile Association
15. August
16. Gloucester
17. Boer War
18. 500
19. *Bambi*
20. Mandarin Chinese
21. France
22. Nicaragua
23. New Zealand (1893)
24. Dover
25. Peter
26. Reagan (69)
27. Ethelwulf (839–858)
28. Strawberries (37/100g)
29. Diphtheria (1 to 5 days)
30. Bassoon

Quiz 67

Knowall's answer: Maureen Lipman
1. Mulder and Scully
2. Derek Jacobi
3. Patrick Moore
4. Tinker and Lady Jane Felsham
5. *Lonesome Dove*
6. *Mastermind*
7. David Attenborough's
8. *Upstairs, Downstairs*
9. *Mr Bean*
10. Geoff Hamilton
11. *Cyber Café*
12. Barry Norman
13. *Out of the Blue*
14. John Lennon
15. An 18-year-old distress signal
16. David Gower
17. Clive James
18. Alan Hansen
19. *Points of View*
20. *Auntie's Sporting Bloomers*
21. *Chicago Hope*
22. *LA Law*
23. Lieutenant Theo Kojak
24. Gary Lineker
25. Ian Richardson
26. *University Challenge*
27. *Steel Magnolias*
28. Jonathan Ross
29. Mystic Meg
30. Dr Beeching's (*Oh Doctor Beeching*)

Quiz 68

Knowall's answer: *TISWAS*
1. *Coronation Street*

2. *Have I Got News For You*
3. Gold Blend coffee
4. *Blind Date*
5. *The Goodies*
6. James Bond
7. 1984
8. *Spitting Image*
9. John Alderton and Pauline Collins
10. Leslie Crowther in *The Price Is Right*
11. *Band of Gold*
12. *Sunday Night at the London Palladium*
13. McGann
14. Don Johnson
15. *Crocodile Shoes* and Finney
16. *Peyton Place*
17. *Cardiac Arrest*
18. Lew Grade
19. *Savannah*
20. Major Kieran Voce and Captain Kate Butler
21. Martin Bashir
22. Chris Evans
23. *Bugs*
24. Harry Enfield
25. *The Sweeney*
26. Stephen Fry
27. *The Muppet Show*
28. Elizabeth Hurley
29. *Market in Honey Lane*
30. First National Lottery numbers drawn on TV

Quiz 69

Knowall's answer: *Rawhide*
1. Hamish MacBeth
2. Crinkly Bottom, Mr Blobby

ANSWERS

3. Peter Mayall
4. *Cathy Come Home*
5. John and David Suchet
6. 1970
7. Himself
8. *To The Manor Born*
9. George Smiley
10. *Murder One*
11. *C.A.T.S. Eyes*
12. *Auf Wiedersehen, Pet*
13. Kenny Everett
14. The Oxo family
15. Lord Thomson of Fleet
16. Violet Carson
17. Bob Hoskins
18. Paul Usher (Barry Grant)
19. *Taggart*
20. Mark Fowler (Todd Carty)
21. Jimmy Savile
22. *Blackadders* (all Rowan Atkinson)
23. *The Magic Roundabout*
24. *The Flintstones*
25. The Prince of Wales
26. *Last of the Summer Wine*
27. Cybill Shepherd and Bruce Willis
28. David Vine, David Coleman
29. Dawn French
30. *Candid Camera*

Quiz 70

Knowall's answer: Sue Ellen's pregnant-by-JR sister Kristin
1. *Eldorado*
2. Trotter
3. *After Henry*
4. Pippa Fletcher (*Home and Away*)

5. Thing (Ted Cassidy)
6. *Men Behaving Badly*
7. Edina "Eddie" Monsoon
8. James Beck (spiv Private James Walker)
9. Two
10. Danny De Vito
11. *Trainer*
12. *Red Dwarf*
13. Cheers Bar (*Cheers*)
14. Noele Gordon
15. *Howard's Way*
16. Sid James
17. Carrington, Colby and Dexter
18. *The Beverly Hillbillies*
19. Victor Meldrew (*One Foot in the Grave*)
20. He raped Kathy Beale
21. Granville
22. *Drop the Dead Donkey*
23. Jack Sugden
24. Wentworth Detention Centre
25. Roseanne Barr, Roseanne Arnold
26. *The Bill*
27. Leonard Rossiter
28. Grundy International

29. Nick Berry
30. Charlton Heston

Quiz 71

Knowall's answer: A red Triumph Roadster
1. David Jason
2. Lynda La Plante
3. *Z Cars*
4. George Baker (to Louise Ramsay)
5. *Serpico*
6. *The Inspector Alleyn Mysteries*
7. "Budgie" Bird (in *Budgie*)
8. John Mortimer
9. *Alfred Hitchcock Presents*
10. *Hill Street Blues*
11. *The Untouchables*
12. Boris Karloff (*Colonel March of Scotland Yard*)
13. Mark McManus
14. Eddie "Fitz" Fitzgerald
15. *Wycliffe*
16. Eddie Shoestring
17. Piet van der Valk
18. Father Frank Dowling
19. Bob Louis and Dave Briggs
20. *Dixon of Dock Green*
21. Marbella, Costa del Sol
22. *The Paradise Club*
23. The one-armed man (Fred Johnson)
24. Perry Mason and Ironside
25. John Thaw and Kevin Whately
26. Robert McCall
27. Fang
28. William Shatner

29. *Twin Peaks*
30. Sean Bean

Quiz 72

Knowall's answer: Alan Rickman
1. Marlon Brando as *The Godfather*
2. *Mary Poppins*
3. Mrs Robinson
4. William Hanna and Joseph Barbera
5. *Let It Be*
6. Barbra Streisand
7. *The Hunchback of Notre Dame*
8. Eddie Murphy
9. *Cape Fear*
10. *Blade Runner*
11. *The Thomas Crown Affair*
12. *A Fistful of Dollars*
13. Dirk Bogarde
14. Burt Bacharach
15. *This Sporting Life*
16. Richard Attenborough
17. *Mission Impossible*
18. The Monty Python team
19. *E.T.: The Extra-Terrestrial*
20. *Stagecoach*
21. Maurice Jarre
22. Kevin Costner
23. *The Third Man*
24. Paul Newman and Robert Redford
25. *Love Story*
26. Kiefer Sutherland (son of Donald)
27. Quentin Tarantino
28. *Goldfinger*
29. Housekeeper Mrs Danvers

30. *Casablanca*

Quiz 73

Knowall's answer:
Jonathan Livingston Seagull
1. Bonnie Parker and Clyde Barrow (*Bonnie and Clyde*)
2. *Trainspotting*
3. Robert Bolt
4. *The Blues Brothers*
5. *The Ten Commandments*
6. Kenya
7. *M*A*S*H*
8. *Anna Karenina*
9. Sharon Stone
10. *Jesus Christ Superstar*
11. *Oklahoma!*
12. *Silence of the Lambs*
13. Richard Benjamin
14. Gabriel Oak
15. Set-piece music-and-dance spectaculars
16. *Zulu*
17. Bernado Bertolucci
18. *The Bridge on the River Kwai*
19. *Lord of the Flies*
20. Elliott Gould
21. *Love Affair*
22. *The Exorcist*
23. Mel Gibson and Danny Glover
24. *Psycho*
25. *The Lion King*
26. *The Battleship Potemkin*
27. *Passport to Pimlico*
28. *The Way We Were*
29. Elmer Bernstein
30. Anthony Asquith

Quiz 74

Knowall's answer:
Peter Sellers
1. Lauren Bacall (in *To Have and Have Not*)
2. Tony Curtis and Janet Leigh
3. Howard Hughes
4. Whoopi Goldberg
5. *Driving Miss Daisy*
6. Fred Astaire
7. George Lucas
8. Burt Lancaster
9. Robert Benchley
10. Marlon Brando
11. John and Roy Boulting
12. Gummo
13. Shirley Temple(-Black)
14. Cartoon voices
15. Errol Flynn
16. Clark Gable (in *The Painted Desert*)
17. Kim Basinger
18. Forrest Gump
19. *White Christmas*
20. Stanley Kubrick
21. "Fatty" Arbuckle
22. Walt Disney
23. James Dean

24. *Zorba the Greek*
25. Terry-Thomas
26. Bette Davis and Joan Crawford
27. Preston Sturges
28. Ingrid Bergman
29. Ginger Rogers
30. *Gone With The Wind*, Vivien Leigh

Quiz 75

Knowall's answer:
Jean Harlow
1. Woody Allen's
2. Nicole Kidman
3. Keystone
4. Roman Polanski
5. Jack Nicholson
6. John Travolta
7. *The French Connection*
8. Jim Henson
9. King Kong
10. "Cubby" Broccoli
11. David, Keith and Robert
12. Peter O'Toole
13. Sidney Poitier
14. Singing cowboy Gene Autry
15. Brigitte Bardot
16. The Barrymores
17. Vincent Price
18. Tatum O'Neal
19. *Some Like It Hot*
20. Bruce and Brandon Lee
21. Cher
22. *The Jazz Singer*
23. Merle Oberon
24. Michelle Pfeiffer
25. Esther Williams
26. Gloria Swanson
27. Leonard Nimoy
28. Charles Pathé

29. Michelangelo Antonioni
30. Nick Nolte

Quiz 76

Knowall's answer:
Edward Elgar
1. Soprano
2. *The Messiah*
3. Oboe
4. George Gershwin
5. Covent Garden
6. Doh, ray, me, fah, soh, la, te, doh
7. *Lohengrin*
8. Slow
9. Hungarian
10. Strauss
11. Royal Albert Hall
12. Classical guitar
13. An aria
14. New York (The Metropolitan Opera)
15. Antonio Stradivari(us)
16. *Sotto voce*
17. London Symphony Orchestra, founded 1904
18. Baby grand
19. Blind from youth
20. The Hallé
21. Canticle
22. Percussion
23. Leeds
24. A group of 19th-century composers (Balakirev, Borodin, Cui, Mussorgsky, and Rimsky-Korsakov) based in St Petersburg
25. José Carreras, Placido Domingo, Luciano Pavarotti
26. Eisteddfod
27. The relative merits of

223

ANSWERS

Italian and French music
28. Tchaikovsky
29. J. S. Bach
30. *The Four Seasons*

Quiz 77

Knowall's answer: *The Ring (of the Nibelungen)*
1. *Chopsticks*
2. A bridge
3. Beethoven
4. *Arabian Nights*
5. The Nutcracker
6. Jacqueline du Pré
7. 5 hours 25 minutes
8. Yehudi Menuhin
9. *Pictures at an Exhibition*
10. *Pizzicato*
11. Diaghilev
12. Debussy
13. *Carnival of the Animals*
14. Dame Margot Fonteyn
15. *Aida*
16. *Peter and the Wolf*
17. Maria Callas
18. Wolfgang Amadeus Mozart
19. A mute

20. *The Planets Op 32* by Gustav Holst
21. John Philip Sousa
22. *Coppélia*
23. Baroque
24. *2001: A Space Odyssey*
25. Borodin
26. Sir Thomas Beecham
27. *Carmina Burana*
28. The Aldeburgh Festival
29. The Coliseum
30. Ralph Vaughan Williams

Quiz 78

Knowall's answer: The "Trout"
1. *The Music Lovers*
2. *The Thieving Magpie*
3. The harp
4. They were all Czechs
5. Bayreuth
6. Egypt
7. Hector Berlioz
8. Soprano, alto, tenor, baritone
9. Benjamin Britten, in 1946
10. Franz Schubert
11. 88 (52 white, 36 black)
12. Bizet's *Carmen*
13. *Scherzo*
14. Beethoven
15. 6th
16. *A Midsummer Night's Dream*
17. Concerto
18. Anton Bruckner
19. Arturo Toscanini
20. The Bachs: ten members were well-known musicians and/or composers, and 64 had

careers in music
21. *La Traviata*, by Verdi – the others are by Puccini
22. The violin
23. *Trumpet Voluntary*
24. Beethoven
25. *The Barber of Seville*
26. Trumpet, trombone, French horn, tuba
27. *Falstaff, Macbeth, Otello*
28. Artur Rubinstein
29. Birdsong
30. Napoleon Bonaparte

Quiz 79

Knowall's answer: Jarvis Cocker
1. Oasis
2. None (in 12 Top Ten hits)
3. Sweden
4. *True*
5. Green and Flynn
6. The Communards, Bronski Beat
7. The Eurythmics
8. Food
9. Dutch
10. Soft Cell
11. Beth Gibbons
12. Micky Dolenz, Mike Nesmith, Peter Tork
13. Little Richard (*Long Tall Sally, Lucille, Good Golly Miss Molly*)
14. 1985
15. He shot John Lennon
16. Olivia Newton-John
17. Chuck Berry
18. *Lily the Pink*
19. Paul Weller
20. *Harvest* (1972)

21. James Brown
22. *The Ballad of John and Yoko*
23. New Orleans (in the single of 1964)
24. *Space Oddity, Ashes to Ashes, Under Pressure, Let's Dance, Dancing in the Street*
25. Alison Moyet
26. New Order
27. *Good Vibrations*
28. Duran Duran
29. The Bay City Rollers
30. Andrew Ridgeley

Quiz 80

Knowall's answer: *Ready, Steady, Go!*
1. Carling
2. Seal – *Seal* (1991) and *Seal* (1994)
3. Montserrat Caballe
4. *Brothers in Arms*
5. *Breaking Glass*
6. Richie Valens and The Big Bopper
7. Carter – The Unstoppable Sex Machine
8. Van Morrison
9. Mr Blobby
10. Queen
11. Jeff Beck, Eric Clapton, Jimmy Page
12. The Cranberries
13. *The Freewheelin' Bob Dylan*
14. *Bat out of Hell*
15. *You're My World*
16. *Itchycoo Park*
17. Degrees (Three – the others are Four)

18. Graham Nash
19. *Ferry 'cross the Mersey*
20. Mariah Carey
21. Enrico Caruso (with *Vesti la giubba* from Leoncavallo's opera *I Paliacci*)
22. Pink Floyd
23. Hootie and the Blowfish
24. Wendy Richard (later Pauline Fowler in *EastEnders*)
25. Supergrass
26. *'Ullo John Got a New Motor?*
27. Celine Dion
28. *Bridge Over Troubled Water*
29. Liam Gallagher of Oasis
30. T. Rex.

Quiz 81

Knowall's answer: Ray Charles
1. Cornet
2. Count Basie
3. Stan Getz
4. BB King
5. John Birks
6. Piano, bass, vibraphone, drums
7. Paul Desmond
8. Belgian
9. Duke Ellington
10. Kenny Ball
11. Charlie Mingus
12. Tenor saxophone and clarinet
13. Dinah Washington
14. Stephane Grappelli
15. F. Scott Fitzgerald
16. Humphrey Lyttleton
17. Jelly Roll Morton

18. Paul Whiteman
19. The Jazz Warriors, The World's First Saxophone Posse
20. Art Tatum
21. Muddy Waters
22. Ella Fitzgerald
23. Thelonius Monk
24. Gene Krupa
25. *When Love Comes To Town*
26. Wynton Marsalis
27. Charlie "Byrd" Parker
28. John Lee Hooker
29. Gerry Mulligan
30. Robert Johnson

Quiz 82

Knowall's answer: Cole Porter (Peru, Indiana!)
1. Leonard Bernstein
2. *Funny Girl*
3. *Porgy and Bess*
4. Eva Perón
5. *Love Me Tender*
6. *South Pacific*
7. Yul Brynner and Deborah Kerr
8. Jacob and Israel
9. *The Sound of Music*
10. Alan Parker
11. Phil Harris (the voice of Baloo)
12. *Bert*
13. T.S. Eliot (*Old Possum's Book of Practical Cats*, 1939)
14. They were three of the 10 films starring Fred Astaire and Ginger Rogers
15. Frank Sinatra
16. Richard Rodgers

17. *Tommy*
18. Ron Moody
19. Johnny Mercer
20. Alan Jay Lerner and Frederick Loewe
21. *Damn Yankees*
22. Paul Robeson
23. Stephen Sondheim
24. *Seven Brides for Seven Brothers*
25. *Les Misérables*
26. Richard and Robert Sherman
27. 1958
28. Joseph in *Joseph and the Amazing Technicolor Dreamcoat*
29. *The Wizard of Oz*
30. Frankie Vaughan

Quiz 83

Knowall's answer: The Ghost Dance
1. A famous tap dancer
2. *Swan Lake*
3. Scottish country dancing
4. *The Loco-motion*
5. Two
6. Castanets
7. The Royal Opera

House, Covent Garden
8. Three
9. Abba
10. *The Nutcracker, The Sleeping Beauty, Swan Lake*
11. The Bluebell Girls
12. A jump
13. Gene Kelly
14. The Lambeth Walk
15. English National Ballet
16. Kenny
17. The Ballets Russes
18. Fred Astaire and Ginger Rogers
19. Chopin
20. South Carolina
21. Red (*The Red Shoes*)
22. Chubby Checker
23. Beryl Grey
24. Andrew Lloyd Webber
25. Dame Margot Fonteyn
26. The Shadows, Kathy Kirby
27. Australian
28. Rudolf Nureyev
29. Dame Ninette de Valois
30. *The Floral Dance*

Quiz 84

Knowall's answer: Decca
1. Midas
2. S
3. 15
4. Emperor Claudius
5. A bank holiday
6. 32°F and 0°C
7. Seven
8. The Soviet *Luna II*
9. Jockey Lester Piggott
10. The 7th Cavalry
11. Lloyds of London
12. The Beaufort Scale

ANSWERS

13. The javelin
14. "Son of Sam"
15. Queen Victoria, in 1837
16. 25 minutes
17. The ox
18. The White House, Washington D.C.
19. Three
20. They're all cheeses
21. Hungary (6-3 in 1953)
22. Quinine
23. Zsa Zsa Gabor
24. François Truffaut
25. A tennis net
26. The Samaritans
27. The Duke of Edinburgh
28. Oldham Athletic
29. 1932
30. The great bustard

Quiz 85

Knowall's answer: Drag racing
1. First woman to ride in the Grand National
2. Persia (now Iran)
3. Silverstone
4. After the yacht *America*, the first winner in 1851
5. The hop, step and jump
6. Allan Border (Australia – 11,174 from 1978 to 1994)
7. USA
8. Ice
9. 8
10. Green
11. Lansdowne Road
12. Rocky Marciano
13. 1948
14. Tony Roche
15. The pole vault

16. Colin Cowdrey
17. Troy, in 1979
18. Aberdeen and Wimbledon
19. Yachting
20. Craig Stadler
21. Light flyweight
22. Sydney Cricket Ground
23. First man to swim the English Channel
24. Wimbledon
25. Jesse Owens
26. The Springboks
27. Jack Johnson
28. Oslo
29. 4 1/4 inches
30. Hanif Mohammed (Karachi v Balawalpur, 1959)

Quiz 86

Knowall's answer: Albatross
1. The Buffalo Bills
2. Ice skating (pairs)
3. McEnroe – he's the only left-hander
4. Wilma Rudolph
5. Phil Hill, Mario Andretti
6. Colin Montgomerie
7. James "Bonecrusher" Smith
8. 434
9. David Campese
10. Greg Norman
11. The time spent batting on 0 – 97 minutes (also a first-class record)
12. 6th
13. Poland
14. Calvin Smith (USA), in the 1988 Olympic

100m final
15. Baseball
16. The three-day event
17. 1,500m (they are, in order, the events comprising the two-day decathlon
18. Seven
19. Martin Offiah
20. Mark Waugh and Michael Atherton
21. Kipchoge ("Kip") Keino
22. Billie-Jean King's
23. Middlesbrough and Sunderland
24. Mike Brearley – the only one born in England!
25. Some experts believed the West German's phenomenal start "cheated the gun"
26. Shooting
27. American Football
28. It was the first to be run by someone over 40!
29. 18
30. 1960

Quiz 87

Knowall's answer: The Formula 1 Williams team
1. Imran Khan (34)
2. Epsom (home of the Derby)
3. Arthur Ashe
4. International Amateur Athletic Federation
5. Britain's Laura Davies
6. Monica Seles (he stabbed her on court)
7. Renaldo Nehemiah
8. Ivan Mauger
9. Henley
10. Jesse Owens
11. Shooting
12. Rod Laver (1968)
13. Ronnie O'Sullivan
14. William Webb Ellis
15. 6
16. John Dawes
17. Jack Hobbs (61,237 at 50.65 between 1905 and 1934)
18. Floyd Patterson
19. Wigan
20. Barclaycard
21. Wilfred Rhodes
22. Jackie Stewart
23. Todd Martin
24. Jansher Khan
25. Rodney Marsh (355, 1970-84)
26. Golf
27. Greg Lemond (1986)
28. West Indian Gordon Greenidge (37,354 runs, 1971-92)
29. Pete Sampras and Steffi Graf
30. Liam Botham

Quiz 88

Knowall's answer:
Julio Iglesias
1. Gary Lineker
2. Union of European Football Associations
3. Gary Ablett
4. The club was founded by two Blackburn Rovers fans
5. Scunthorpe United
6. Stanley Matthews (1965)
7. Vienna
8. Derby County
9. Rochdale (1962)
10. Lincoln City, Watford, Aston Villa, Wolves
11. Jimmy Greaves' clubs (he scored on his debut for each)
12. Ipswich Town
13. Norman Whiteside (17 years 42 days, for N. Ireland in 1982)
14. Atletico Bilbao
15. Queen's Park Rangers (1981)
16. Volgograd
17. Jurgen Klinsmann (after scoring for Spurs)
18. Falkirk
19. Preston North End
20. Alan Shearer
21. Charlton, Oldham, Wigan
22. Bobby Robson
23. Maracaña Stadium, Rio de Janeiro (199,589 in 1950)
24. 8
25. Tottenham Hotspur, Cup Winners Cup, 1963
26. Graeme Souness
27. Manchester United (beat Red Star Belgrade)
28. Howard Wilkinson
29. Alan Sunderland
30. 13 points (Everton over Liverpool, 1985)

Quiz 89

Knowall's answer: They were all on the beaten side in the FA Cup final
1. Roger Hunt (England's 1966 World Cup winning team)
2. Alan Ball (Manchester City)
3. Northampton Town (1961-69)
4. They were all runners-up in their leagues
5. Gordon Cowans, Paul Rideout
6. It was the first televised League match (Blackpool v Bolton in 1960 was a one-off experiment)
7. Scotland's
8. Kenny Dalglish, after leaving Blackburn
9. Gianni Rivera and "Gigi" Riva
10. Neil Sullivan (Wimbledon)
11. Morocco
12. Derry City
13. Hoddle: he went to France, the rest to Italy
14. Kevin Moran
15. Amarildo
16. Everton
17. Bert Trautmann

(Manchester City)
18. Brazil
19. Kevin Keegan
20. Hampden Park, Glasgow (136,505, Celtic v Leeds, 1970)
21. Ted Drake
22. Tommy Hutchison (1981), Gary Mabbutt (1987)
23. Argentina, Colombia, Spain
24. Willie Johnston
25. 3 – a semi-final penalty and two to Germany in the final
26. Ruud Krol
27. 13 – a finals record
28. George Graham
29. Italy (1934, 1990), Mexico (1970, 1986). France (1938) joins them in 1998
30. Huddersfield Town's

Quiz 90

Knowall's answer: Lotus
1. Michelle Smith
2. Orange

3. Carl Lewis (USA)
4. Nadia Comaneci (Romania, on the assymmetric bars)
5. 36th
6. They gave a gloved black power salute on the victory rostrum
7. Vassily Alexeyev
8. The marathon
9. Bob Beamon
10. Baron de Coubertin
11. Steve Cram
12. The 385 yards was added to bring the start to beneath the royal children's window at Windsor Castle
13. Greg Louganis (USA) in the springboard diving
14. He was known as the "Flying Finn"
15. Evander Holyfield
16. The "Fosbury Flop", by Dick Fosbury (USA)
17. *Chariots of Fire*
18. The USA: they beat France in 1924, the last time the sport was included
19. Peter Snell
20. In protest at the Soviet invasion of her country
21. Dutch
22. Florence Griffith-Joyner ("Flo-Jo" – USA)
23. Emil Zatopek: it was his first marathon!
24. 1916, 1940, 1944
25. Al Oerter (USA) in the discus, 1956-68
26. 1988
27. Kenny Harrison

ANSWERS

28. Swimmer Dawn Fraser, in 1964
29. After collapsing four times only yards from the finish he was helped over the line by an official
30. The athletes performed naked

Quiz 91

Knowall's answer: Babe Ruth or simply "The Babe"
1. The Dallas Cowboys
2. He invented basketball
3. Ice hockey
4. Six
5. The Rosebowl, Pasadena
6. Jesse Owens, because he was black
7. The Chicago Bulls
8. Don Larsen
9. The Detroit Lions
10. Tennis
11. Augusta, Georgia
12. The Cleveland Indians
13. He scored 100 points in one NBA game

14. Joe DiMaggio
15. The Anaheim Mighty Ducks
16. Montreal Expos, Toronto Blue Jays
17. Carl Lewis
18. 1967, The Green Bay Packers
19. The Harlem Globetrotters
20. Alexei Lalas (Padova)
21. The New York Yankees
22. Professional wrestling
23. Indycar racing
24. First African-American to play in the Major League
25. Arnold Palmer
26. The Islanders, the Rangers
27. The Buffalo Bills
28. The New York Cosmos
29. William Perry, the London Monarchs
30. Three 20-minute periods

Quiz 92

Knowall's answer: Foil (the others are epée and sabre)
1. 15
2. Gymnastics: it's a type of vault
3. 147
4. Eton, Rugby
5. 7
6. J
7. 28
8. Red: the players' caps are dark blue or white
9. Three: white, white spot and red
10. A flush

11. Table tennis: it is the men's world team championship
12. "Sounds like"
13. Ice hockey
14. Snatch (one movement), clean and jerk (two movements)
15. Two
16. Jahangir Khan
17. Gloucestershire (at Badminton House, seat of the Duke of Beaufort)
18. The Old Kent Road
19. Jayne Torvill and Christopher Dean: it was their fourth successive title
20. Keith Deller
21. Terry Allcock and David Bryant
22. Blackjack
23. Dennis Taylor
24. Bridge
25. Badminton 15, squash 9, table tennis 21
26. The bishop
27. Judo
28. A "backgammon"
29. Norwegian
30. The vault and the floor exercises

Quiz 93

Knowall's answer: Linford Christie
1. Ivan Goranisevic
2. Tony Jacklin (1970)
3. Swim the English Channel
4. 29 – a record
5. Zola Budd

6. Jonah Barrington (1973)
7. Louison Bobet (the others have all won the Tour de France a record five times – he won three in a row 1953-5)
8. Ken Norton
9. Sebastian Coe
10. He was 55 – the oldest man ever to win a Formula 1 GP race
11. Sean Kerly
12. Ken Rosewall (1954 and 1974)
13. Jon Ridgeon
14. Badminton
15. Chris Boardman
16. He won the Italian Grand Prix in a Ferrari
17. Eric Bristow
18. Ingrid Christiansen (Norway)
19. Jimmy White: (a) he's left-handed (b) he has never won the world snooker title
20. Tony Sailer (1956), Jean-Claude Killy (1968)
21. Steve Cauthen
22. It was the first "million-dollar gate"
23. Bill Beaumont
24. Armin Hary (West Germany)
25. Wasim Akram
26. Boris Becker
27. Rocky Marciano
28. Rob Andrew
29. Graham Gooch
30. Brian London

Quiz 94

Knowall's answer:
Mrs (Isabella) Beeton
1. The sturgeon
2. Rolex
3. The diamond
4. Potatoes or grain
5. Australia
6. ME (Myalgic encephalomyelitis)
7. Gerald Ratner of Ratners
8. Coco Chanel
9. Bordeaux
10. The sable
11. A last
12. Oliver Cromwell
13. None of these – it's served raw
14. Force-fed goose's liver
15. Champagne
16. Angora goats
17. The Filofax
18. The sloe
19. The 16th century
20. Platinum
21. A pavlova (after Anna Pavlova)
22. Sherry and port

23. Ossie Clark
24. Imelda Marcos
25. The ostrich
26. Château d'Yquem
27. Cooked snails
28. BSE (Bovine spongiform encephalopathy)
29. The Mini-Moke
30. Winston Churchill

Quiz 95

Knowall's answer:
The elder
1. Rum
2. Las Vegas
3. Basil
4. Corn flakes
5. Havana cigars
6. The Body Shop
7. Ice cream
8. 1979
9. The almond
10. Aromatherapy
11. Oysters
12. Vodka and tomato juice
13. Shaker
14. The potato
15. Teddy Boys
16. Henry J. Heinz
17. Cannabis (marijuana)
18. Coca-Cola
19. Suet and oatmeal
20. Downsizing
21. 1893 (in Chicago)
22. *Beaujolais nouveau*
23. Len Deighton
24. Cosmetics and toiletries
25. Borsch
26. Mary Quant
27. Campbell's
28. Rice
29. Biba
30. A derby

Quiz 96

Knowall's answer:
Pottery
1. People interested in film
2. Butterflies
3. Birdwatcher Bill Oddie
4. Origami
5. Sail (they are dinghies)
6. A stamp collector
7. 36
8. Fantasy Role Playing
9. Pedigree cats
10. Thelwell
11. Wine
12. Embroidery stitch
13. The coarse fishing season
14. Rock climbing
15. Cryptic crosswords
16. A painter
17. Japanese flower arranging
18. The Pennine Way
19. The kitchen
20. "Empty fist"
21. Sixpenny purple of 1904
22. Hinduism
23. Campaign for Real Ale
24. A trainspotter
25. Jumping off buildings with a parachute
26. Weaving
27. Antiques (and prices)
28. Four
29. Knotted thread or cord
30. A numismatist

Quiz 97

Knowall's answer:
Narcissus
1. Foxglove
2. Roses

3. Clematis
4. Topiary
5. Wormwood
6. May
7. The tomato
8. Potatoes
9. Turkey
10. Busy Lizzie
11. Aphids
12. Acid
13. Heather
14. A blunt tool for making planting holes in soil
15. Apple
16. The potato
17. Vita Sackville-West
18. Chamomile
19. A hybrid
20. Angelica
21. Onions
22. Bindweed
23. The branches are trained horizontally
24. Grape vines
25. John Innes
26. Succulents and cacti
27. Able to survive frost
28. Vegetables
29. Fuchsia
30. Bonsai

Quiz 98

Knowall's answer: Mickey (Walt Disney was persuaded to change it by his wife)
1. When he changed from Dr David Banner into The Incredible Hulk
2. The horse chestnut
3. The piano
4. Paul Nicholls
5. Bending the legs

ANSWERS

6. Gene Hackman
7. Darling
8. Judge Dredd
9. Tony Robinson
10. *Snow White and the Seven Dwarfs* (1937)
11. Fred
12. Nothing – it was bare
13. Maplins
14. Otis
15. They were all created by Phil Redmond
16. In *Byker Grove*
17. *Junior Masterchef*
18. Dr Who
19. The piccolo
20. Icelandic
21. Chop suey
22. The turkey who lived on the hill
23. An alley-cat (in *The Aristocats*)
24. Aesop
25. David Bowie
26. Red and white
27. Babar
28. Signourey Weaver
29. A vacuum cleaner
30. Holby General

Quiz 99

Knowall's answer:
Beatrix Potter
1. Dangerous driving
2. The Spice Girls
3. Bread and honey
4. She was crushed by Dorothy's house
5. Thomas the Tank Engine
6. Supergran
7. 40,000
8. Dick King-Smith

9. Basil Brush
10. The fox and the cat
11. Giant Haystacks
12. Whether to chop off the broad or narrow end of a boiled egg
13. The heart of a deer
14. Butcher, baker and candlestick-maker
15. They roll in coal dust
16. Simba and Scar
17. A chicken bone
18. The Smurfs: *I've Got a Little Puppy*
19. 10,000
20. Denmark
21. Mr Twit was making her walking stick progressively longer
22. Sebastian
23. Knight is not a member of TV's *Gladiators*
24. Because the mayor failed to pay him for ridding the town of rats
25. Stephanie
26. *David Copperfield*
27. Reverend Green
28. *Wizadora*
29. Randy Newman
30. Robbie Williams

Quiz 100

Knowall's answer: **Mull**
1. Seven
2. Cat's-eye road studs
3. France
4. Bobby Moore, Geoff Hurst and Martin Peters
5. 35 years
6. Renault
7. Wellington, New Zealand

8. John and Walter Huston
9. Amen
10. The vanilla plant
11. Carbon-14 dating
12. Paris
13. 9%
14. Gordon Richards
15. The Second Severn Crossing
16. America's Ivy League universities
17. General Charles de Gaulle
18. Microwaves

19. 42
20. They're beside the sea
21. Thomas Fairfax
22. Los Angeles
23. Mustard
24. They're all Quarks
25. First men to row the Atlantic
26. It is silent
27. Pakistan
28. Jersey
29. 29
30. A cricket bat

THAT'S ALL FOLKS !!!

Every effort has been made to ensure that questions and answers are accurate, but the Authors cannot warrant that the content is completely error-free. Comments and suggestions are welcome, and may be mailed to Scribble Ink at:
4 The Old Maltings, Nethergate Street, Hopton, Diss, Norfolk IP22 2QZ.